Thomas Ford Memorial Library

HOURS

Monday through Friday 1:30-5:00 & 7:00-9:00
Saturday 10:00-12:00 & 1:30-5:00

Thunderstorm

Also by Thelma Harrington Bell

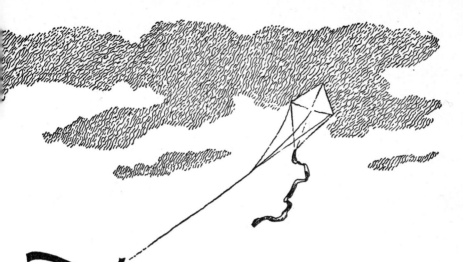

Thunderstorm

by THELMA HARRINGTON BELL

Illustrated by CORYDON BELL

THE VIKING PRESS · New York

PRINTED IN THE U. S. A. BY THE VAIL-BALLOU PRESS, INC.

To Michael, Jeremy, and Brian
who enjoy the whimsical opinion of
Katisha
when she sings:

Volcanos have a splendour that is grim,
And earthquakes only terrify the dolts,
But to him who's scientific
There is nothing that's terrific
In the falling of a flight of thunderbolts!

and of Ko-Ko
when he replies:

Yes, in spite of all my meekness,
If I have a little weakness,
It's a passion for a flight of thunderbolts.

in *The Mikado* by W. S. Gilbert

CONTENTS

7

1. MYTHS AND TRUTHS

Clouds, Winds, and Skyfire

It is a hot, still, sultry summer day. The early-morning sky was clear and blue, and the dawn air fresh and cool. But now, at ten o'clock, the sun is pouring down its burning rays, heating the already warm earth. Tufts of clouds that appeared almost unnoticed at first in the sky have grown to high, billowing mounds, piled up brilliantly white against the blue tent of the heavens. Some of the clouds resemble enormous cauliflower heads, quite firm and solid. They seem to hang motionless like cut-outs against the vivid sky.

By early afternoon the cloud heaps have increased in number and they have taken on an appearance of activity. Changes are occurring in their silhouettes. One or two of them are reminiscent of lofty, massive castles with towers and turrets pushing up from a central keep. A rumble of thunder breaks the stillness. One of the clouds has moved in our direction. We can no longer see the top of its white battlements now, because it is almost overhead and hidden by stretching layers of vapor looking like blue-shadowed cotton. Even the sun is hidden.

The base of the cloud, which forms a low, ragged ceiling

over the land, looks dark and threatening. Suddenly, there
is a startling flash of lightning, and the clap of thunder that
follows the flash sounds menacingly near. A strong cool
wind, blowing out from the front of the approaching storm,
springs up. The sky grows ever darker and more ominous.
Large raindrops splatter down as we run for shelter—and
just in time, too.

A great slanting shower of heavy drops sweeps down,
riding a strong gust of wind. Now the lightning flashes are
very close, and the thunder booms like cannon with echoing
blasts that all but shake the house. Doors slam. Windows
begin to steam from the effect of the breath of the cool storm
wind on the window panes, which are warm from the air of
the house. There is a sudden shower of small hailstones
mixed with the rain. On the lawn collects a scattered litter
of leaves and twigs torn off by the strong gusts of the wind.

This is the intimate, the personal view of the thunderstorm, that exciting exhibition of weather that is nature's
most powerful and complex manifestation. Even its dimen-
sions are outsize. The storm cloud may tower above the
earth to a height of from six to ten miles, making the
tallest mountain look small by comparison. As it moves over
the land, a single thunderstorm can cover sixty square miles
with its dark canopy.

If we could fly an extra-sturdy aircraft on a sightseeing
trip into the great cloud of a mature thunderstorm, we would
experience a startling variety of sights and sensations. We
might find ourselves in vertical blasts of wind that would toss
our plane thousands of feet aloft in a matter of seconds.
These upsweeping drafts of warm air in especially severe

storms may reach a velocity of 150 miles an hour. In contrast, there are strong downsweeping cold winds that pour rain out on the earth with the force of a super-gigantic fire hose.

High in the cloud we would run into churning fogs made of microscopic ice crystals, as well as blizzards of snow. We might be deluged by torrents of rain and pelted by hailstones as large as baseballs. The storm cloud is not content to manufacture just these hydrometeors—as snow crystals, hailstones, and rain are called. It also manufactures electricity in enormous quantities. Our plane might collect electrical charges that would stream off wing tips and propeller blades in bluish, brushlike flames known as Saint Elmo's fire.

These discharges of static electricity received their name long ago from Mediterranean sailors, who often observed mysterious flames flaring from the mastheads of their ships when a thunderstorm was near. Since the flames did no harm, the sailors considered them an omen that there was nothing to fear from the storm, and attributed their good luck to the patron saint of sailors, Saint Elmo, who was Peter Gonzales, a Spanish monk living toward the close of the twelfth century.

But on a trip through a thunderstorm cloud we would encounter more electrical flames than those of Saint Elmo's fire. We would probably see blinding bolts of lightning. This electrical force is quite another story from that of Saint Elmo's gentle display, for lightning represents millions of volts of electricity. It travels from place to place in a cloud, or from cloud to earth, at a speed of about 20,000 miles per second, or approximately one-tenth the speed of light. And the heat it generates for a small fraction of a second is greater than that on the surface of the sun. Unbelievable as it may seem, the power of a single bolt of lightning is about equal to that of ten million railroad locomotives.

Adding up all the forces that go to make up the energy of the great storm machine—the lifting of water vapor into the atmosphere, the winds, the making of snow, hail, and rain, and the generation of electricity—produces a stupendous sum of power. The work of these natural forces in one storm can represent one hundred times more power than did the type of atomic bomb that was dropped on Japan during the Second World War.

Early Superstitions

Primitive man knew no arithmetic and seldom questioned what he saw; but he early learned to have an awesome respect for the swift, destructive flashes of lightning that darted to earth from low, windy clouds. He even feared the booming thunder that accompanied the storm. Since there were no scientists to explain the workings of nature, superstition often took the place of knowledge. To ancient peoples, the roar of thunder was the work of unseen gods or other supernatural authority. In those long-ago centuries, it is not surprising to find that these primitive notions about thunderbolts created many strange practices and beliefs that seem utterly fantastic and nonsensical to us of the twentieth century.

Because lightning was supposed to have magic powers—

and dark magic at that—persons struck by a bolt from a storm who managed to survive were looked upon as evil, and were made to undergo long ceremonies that would cleanse them of the curse of the fire from the sky. Those who were killed by a lightning stroke were buried as soon as possible and without funeral rites, because they were thought to have brought down upon themselves the wrath of angry gods. For the same reason, cattle or wild game killed by a bolt of lightning were never used for food, even if the people of a tribe or community were desperately hungry.

Carrying these ideas even further, travelers went out of their way to avoid a lightning-struck tree; and no peasant ever cut a "blasted oak" for firewood, because the thundery magic in the wood might bring on all manner of evil and disaster. Even as recently as in our own well-informed decade, the 1950s, some people of the southern Appalachians declare that lightning-struck wood will not burn in a stove or fireplace. It will only smoke and "sob." And the burning of sassafras wood is especially to be avoided, because to do so will "draw thunder." If one tries to get at the bottom of this superstition and asks a mountain man why he thinks this is so, he merely replies that everyone knows it to be true. (I have burned plenty of sassafras without bringing lightning down the chimney!)

Thunder Gods

In ancient times, peoples of every nation held among their beliefs the idea that some one of their gods rode the storm and held the power of the dreaded flaming bolt of white fire under his control. In Egypt, it was the god of evil, Set, who cast bolts of lightning to the earth at his pleasure. This seems rather strange, since Egypt was probably a land of few thunderstorms then, as it is today. Early Oriental sculptors who created stone images of Buddha often placed in his right hand an object called a Vajra. This was the symbol of the thunderbolt—a short bar with jagged prongs at each end.

Far to the north in the ancient world, the Norsemen created Thor as their god of thunderstorms. This fierce deity with flaming red hair carried a magic hammer which he hurled to earth on a streak of lightning as he rode in a chariot drawn by two goats. The running of the chariot wheels upon the high, anvil-topped storm clouds was thought to cause the thunder. Thor's hammer, called Mjöllner, always returned to his hand, and thus was always ready for use as another thunderbolt with which to destroy his eternal foes, the giants.

Like the peasants of long ago, Scandinavian farmers of today sometimes turn up with their plows bits of iron or stone which they say are broken pieces of Thor's hammerhead. They call these pieces "thunder-stones," but they have proved to be nothing more curious than small meteorites or long-buried tools of Old Stone Age people. Thor still survives in the name of one of our weekdays: Thor's Day, or, as we know it, Thursday.

The lightning flashes that burst from tall dark clouds over ancient Greece and Italy also were thought to be of divine origin. Anything so violent and terrifying must be supernatural. In fact, the citizens of Athens and Rome looked upon the thunderbolt as a sign that the father of the gods was greatly displeased.

In Greece it was Zeus, and in Italy it was Jupiter, or Jove, who sent down the forked lightning to punish sinful people or to destroy their houses. Zeus not only hurled down thunderbolts to crush emperors and commoners alike who had offended him, but was also quite ready to bring on a thunderstorm to help a favored army that was in peril of losing a battle.

Although they would have been the last to admit it, the superstitious Romans made even more of thunder magic than did the Greeks. The results of this supposed wrath of the gods took on varied aspects. For instance, graves of persons struck by lightning were dug on the spot where they died, and became local shrines dedicated to Jupiter's rushing fire. And it was against the law for houses or temples damaged by the sacred bolt ever to be repaired or rebuilt.

No one had ever seen a laurel bush struck by lightning, and so this shrub, sacred to Apollo, was thought to be immune. The Emperor Tiberius, who reigned during the time of Christ, and who was desperately frightened by thunder, took this belief very much to heart. He kept laurel wreaths always within easy reach, and wore one on his head as a protection during a thunderstorm. He must have been cautious in other ways, because there is no record of his ever being struck by a thunderbolt.

Nowadays, superstitious notions about lightning and thunder and their causes survive only among people who have not yet caught up with the vast store of knowledge that modern science provides. When the white man came to plant his colonies in America, the native Indians regarded nature in the light of strange and magical beliefs, since many things they experienced could be explained only in terms of the work of spirits. Living primitively out under the sky, they felt the full power of storms. They imagined that the lightning was a great, swift white bird that darted to earth from the stormy sky, carrying with it the smell of brimstone. Thunder was the beating of its broad wings.

The American Indians no longer hold to their old beliefs about the thunderbird, but, far across the world in southeastern Africa, a fearsome bird that brings lightning and thunder is very real to some tribes of a race of Negroes called Bantu. The Bantus, who live in an area that includes Southern Rhodesia, between the Zambezi and Limpopo rivers, are a people of very ancient but still primitive culture. Their witch-doctors, of course, cling to the old myths and religious magic. If a large tree should be shattered by lightning, a search may be made for the droppings, or possibly the eggs of the thunderbird, which might hatch into more birds of destruction. The tree itself is looked upon as possessing evil magic, and is an object always to be avoided.

Two Billion Years Ago

Thunderstorms are almost as old as earth itself. A solid crust formed on our planet not more than two billion years ago, when the young earth was still too hot to retain liquid water on its surface. Practically all of its supply of water was contained in a thick, warm, swirling mass of clouds that covered the globe completely. As ages passed and the earth and the atmosphere above it cooled, rain began to fall on the bare rock crust. It rained continuously for century upon century from the clouds of enormous storms that certainly must have been accompanied by furious lightning and ear-shattering thunder.

Rivers of water cut their way to the deep hollows in the planet's cooling surface, and thus the seas and oceans were formed. These great bodies of water were probably in existence about one thousand million years ago, by which time earth's weather had more or less settled down to a pattern in which storm and fair skies succeeded each other much as they do today.

Thunderstorms have not changed their fiery habits since the days of our very primitive ancestors, but people no longer think of them as the work of wrathful gods or darting birds. They are recognized as familiar parts of the variegated weather nature provides. Just as scientists have solved many of the mysteries connected with the vast streams of wind and cloud that forever circulate around the spinning earth, so they have learned a great deal about the formation and habits of the greatest of all weather machines—the thunderstorm.

2. THE BUILDING OF A THUNDERHEAD

Sun, Water, and Wind

The only common liquid on earth is water. Without it there would be no rivers and oceans, no clouds, and no living thing on this planet. Water is also the only common substance that exists in all three stages—vapor, liquid, and solid—in the ordinary air temperatures in which we live. We breathe it as a vapor, drink it and bathe in it as a liquid, and skate on it as a solid. We also play in it as snow, which, of course, is a solid, too. An amazing thing about water is that it is constantly changing from one state to another all over the world.

Clouds are the joint work of three familiar things, sun, water, and air, which, working together, release an unbelievable amount of energy over the surface of the earth through the transfer from one place to another of that invisible speck of matter, the water molecule. As you may know, two atoms of hydrogen and one atom of oxygen combine to form one molecule of the chemical compound water. These molecules, in numbers so vast that we cannot even imagine them, are forever moving through what the scientists speak of as the closed cycle of evaporation, condensation, and precipitation.

The original source of all the energy that keeps this "water cycle" in motion is the sun. Heat from its rays evaporates water from oceans, lakes, rivers, and land, and draws warm vapor up into the air above the earth. You can see the effect of evaporation if you place a shallow pan of water where the sun can strike it. In quite a short space of time the liquid water will have disappeared into the surrounding air as vapor. In liquid water, molecules are packed fairly close together; but during the process of evaporation they escape from one another and move about freely in the air.

When water is in the form of vapor, it exists as a gas which we cannot see, even though the air around us may be saturated with it, as it often is on "damp" days both in summer and in winter. Under the right conditions, however, the water molecules of vapor join together to form tiny droplets of water which are visible. We can see this process on a cold day when the warm vapor of our breath, which is invisible, condenses and appears as a little cloud which quickly evaporates into the surrounding air.

Condensation is the opposite of evaporation. Instead of moving away from one another, as they do in the process of evaporation, water molecules during condensation collect into tiny dense bundles. When a large quantity of warm, moist air or vapor rises high into the atmosphere above the earth, it cools in expansion and the invisible vapor condenses on microscopic particles of dust that are always floating in the atmosphere. The droplets of liquid water that are formed by this process of condensation are very small, so small in fact that about ten thousand of them could be laid in a row across the head of an ordinary pin. But, crowded together in a dense mass, the droplets at once become visible and form the clouds we see in the sky.

Clouds in the middle and lower levels of the atmosphere consist entirely of these liquid water droplets. Clouds in higher levels above the earth—like the cirrus (often called "mares' tails") and the tops of mature thunderheads—are composed of water in the form of small ice crystals.

The third part of the water cycle is, of course, precipitation, the falling of rain, sleet, snow, and hail from the clouds. This happens when tiny droplets of cloud water, under various atmospheric conditions, work to build raindrops and snow crystals heavy enough to fall from cloud to earth. Hailstones manufactured by thunderclouds usually grow large enough to reach the ground rapidly and without too much melting; but snow crystals, being feathery and fragile, quickly melt to drops of rain as they fall into lower and warmer air. Consequently, snow never falls to earth from a thunderstorm.

The handsome thunderhead is a type of cloud which weathermen call cumulonimbus, a name meaning a heaped-up cloud that produces rain. It is the tallest of all clouds. Its base may be only a few thousand feet over our heads, but its top can sometimes rise to more than fifty thousand feet above the earth.

The most familiar type of thundercloud is the kind we see during the summer when the days are sunny and hot and the air is fairly moist with water vapor. The sun, strange to say, does not directly warm the air that surrounds the earth to any appreciable extent. Instead, its rays heat the ground, and this reflected heat warms the moist air close to the earth. As the air is heated it becomes lighter and more unstable than the cooler air above, so that it rises like great bubbles into the upper atmosphere, where there is lower atmospheric pressure. Here the bubbles have room to expand, and as they expand they cool, just as the air under pressure in a tire expands and cools when it is let out of the valve. When it cools sufficiently, the moisture in the air condenses into droplets of liquid water. Weathermen have a name for the cool layer of air where vapor is converted into liquid water. They call it the condensation level. From the ground, this level appears to us as the base of the cloud.

This constant rising of warm, moist air into the cloud that has formed creates a draft that, when it becomes strong enough, acts like the draft in a tall chimney and begins to draw into its stream moist earth-heated air from miles around. You may have noticed the action of smoke coming from factory chimney stacks in an industrial area over which a thunderhead is forming. If you have, you will recall that the smoke seemed to be drifting toward the underside of the cloud from all directions. It was being drawn toward the upsweeping draft in the great chimney of the cloud itself.

Whether over city or countryside, this rising of warm, moist air from the earth builds large islands or banks of dense, puffy white cloud. On a summer's day one can often see a number of these cumulus clouds moving slowly through the sky late in the morning. Every thunderstorm begins as a cumulus cloud, but only a small number of the towering cumulus clouds we see will actually grow into storms of rain and lightning. Whether or not an individual cloud will develop into a cumulonimbus depends upon conditions in the immediate atmosphere.

As the sun climbs higher in the heavens and the day grows hotter, some of these cumulus clouds may start to grow, pushing their mounds of white far up into the sky. Something seems to be happening inside the clouds, too. Their tops billow and churn slowly like thick white steam. Protuberances often sprout from their sides. In fact, the clouds seem alive, and almost ready to burst with energy. A low rumble of thunder tells us that a thunderstorm is active inside the group of clouds; and, if the winds aloft are right, the storm may travel in our direction and present us with rain, cool gusts of wind, and the flashing fireworks of lightning.

Since we have no plane, and are certainly not pilots experienced enough to fly into a growing thunderhead and observe for ourselves what is going on, we shall have to be content with making a diagrammatic trip aloft.

The First Phase

To begin this sky adventure on paper, we will look into a single cumulus cloud such as we might see on a late summer morning. At the left of the diagram in Figure A are indicated various levels in the atmosphere above the earth in thousands of feet. At the right are the Fahrenheit temperatures we should be likely to find at these levels.

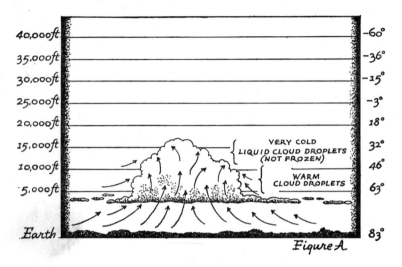

Figure A

It is quite a warm day close to the earth. Here the temperature is about 83 degrees, according to the thermometer on the porch, and much hotter in the sun. We can see by the diagram, however, that the temperature normally becomes colder and colder the higher above the earth we go. At 15,000 feet the temperature of the air is at freezing, or 32 degrees. At 40,000 feet the air is very cold indeed. Up there the temperature is 60 below zero!

In the diagram, the black arrows show the direction of the wind currents formed by warm, moist air rising into the atmosphere. The cloud, of course, is not flat, but has a shape roughly resembling a dome-shaped ball of cotton. The winds are actually coming in from all points of the compass.

Water vapor carried by the ascending air has condensed into cloud droplets at about 5000 feet, where the air temperature is a cool 63 degrees. This is the level at which the base of the cloud has formed. But more and more light warm air

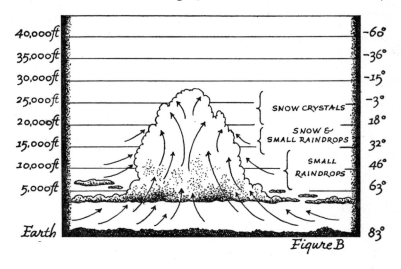

40,000ft	-60°
35,000ft	-36°
30,000ft	-15°
25,000ft	-3°
20,000ft	SNOW CRYSTALS 18°
15,000ft	SNOW & SMALL RAINDROPS 32°
10,000ft	SMALL RAINDROPS 46°
5,000ft	63°
Earth	83°

Figure B

has pushed up beyond the base and has converted its water vapor into liquid droplets. The top of the cloud has reached beyond 15,000 feet, where the air is at the freezing temperature. Here the cloud droplets are very cold, but they are still in the form of water. Although they would *like* to freeze into crystals of ice, the conditions in the cloud are not yet quite right for these cold droplets to turn into ice or snow.

While we have been watching, our cloud has grown quite a little. Its former hard, clear outlines have softened, and its top has taken on a kind of bright sheen that is characteristic of ice clouds. The bottom of the cloud is still at the same level, and more "shelf clouds," or stratus sheets, have spread out from the base. But look at the puffy top! It has shot up to about 25,000 feet, because of strong updrafts that may reach speeds of 40 or 50 miles an hour in the upper portions of the cloud.

Only fifteen or twenty minutes ago the cloud was a simple

mass of tiny cloud droplets. Now, with its top at a temperature of three or more degrees below zero, a multitude of
ice and snow crystals have formed; and, as they grow
heavier, they will fall into the middle levels of the cloud and
will help to trigger off the formation of more snow crystals.
Small raindrops, too, have appeared in the lower half of the
cloud.

But one should not get the impression that the inside of
a cumulus cloud is a quiet place. The storm machine is
actually speeding up. Great gusty bubbles of warm, moist
air are rising within it; and not only are they supplying
more and more vapor for condensation, but they are helping
to churn and break up the rapidly growing numbers of snow
crystals and raindrops. Light, moisture-laden air is being
sucked into the cloud at its sides as well as from below as the
updrafts increase in speed. The buoyancy of this rising air
is not alone responsible for the powerful updrafts in the
maturing thunderhead. Extra energy is added to the uprising
air when cloud droplets are formed from water vapor.

Water vapor, as we know, contains a quantity of heat
which it gains when it evaporates from liquid water. On the
other hand, when water vapor condenses, it gives back its
stored heat to the surrounding air, and, of course, warms it.
Some notion of what this warming amounts to can be
grasped when it is realized that the heat produced in con-
densing enough water vapor to create 1 inch of rain over 1
square mile of land is equivalent to burning 6500 tons of
coal, or about 1 million gallons of fuel oil.

In a thunderhead the amount of this heat of condensation given to uprising air is sufficient to keep it lighter than

the cooler air it displaces. Because of this, the updraft of warm air pushes higher and higher. This extra ascent occurs in spite of further cooling due to expansion as the air rises into the cold upper atmosphere.

Pushing to 35,000

The storm machine is really humming now with increasing energy. Its head, pushing up toward the 35,000-foot level, encloses a snowstorm; its middle section is a gusty mixture of snow, raindrops, and perhaps hailstones. None of these hydrometeors can fall from the cloud, because they are not yet heavy enough to escape from the powerful upsurging winds that act as one-way elevators.

Not only is the cloud growing larger by the accumulation of vast amounts of water vapor, but from this vapor it is manufacturing snow and rain by the ton. The snow crystals and raindrops are not given a moment's rest. As they madly swirl and toss they bump into one another and break up. But soon the bits and pieces are stealing more water droplets from the cloud in an effort to develop into full-fledged snow crystals and raindrops again. All of this bumping, rubbing, and breaking up is accomplishing something else: it is probably contributing to the generation of large charges of electricity which the cloud is busily storing up.

To judge by its appearance in Figure C, the cumulonimbus is developing into a first-class thunderstorm. In the fifteen minutes or so since we diagramed it in Figure B, the cloud has thrust its great white summit to more than 40,000 feet above the earth. All its machinery is working powerfully

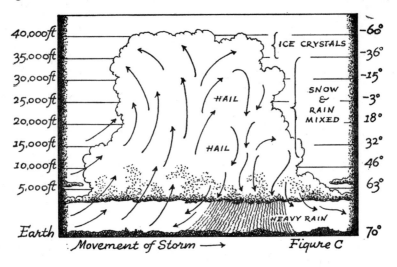

Movement of Storm →   *Figure C*

and at top speed. And the whole storm cloud is moving over the land at perhaps 20 miles per hour, blown along by the prevailing winds aloft.

Liquid droplets of water that wanted to freeze but could not when they were at 15,000 feet, have been whisked up into a layer of air where the temperature is 36 degrees and more below zero. Here they have no choice but to evaporate and quickly reassemble their chilly molecules into ice and snow crystals.

The hordes of raindrops in the middle and lower portions of the cloud meanwhile have been milling about in the updraft. The cloud is so thick with rain that small individual drops have joined one another in collision to form much larger and heavier drops. They have become so heavy, in fact, that they are defying their jailer, the updraft. In the forward part of the storm we can see that great swarms of the heavy drops have escaped from the clutches of the up-

sweeping winds and are pouring to earth from the base of
the cloud in a drenching torrent of rain. The heaviest part
of the fall, in what is sometimes called a "cloudburst" or
"gullywasher," may be concentrated over little more than a
square mile of land as the storm moves along. In a short
space of time as much as one and one-half inches of rain
can fall on this area. Cloudburst is a good term for such a
Niagara of rain: one and one-half inches of rain over one
square mile would weigh over a hundred thousand tons!

As the rain falls from the cloud it creates a strong draft
of its own. This time it is a downdraft, and as more and more
rain falls, this downsweeping wind spreads out over a greater
area.

The period of heavy rain marks the time of greatest activity in the life of a thunderstorm. Our cumulonimbus cloud
is literally bursting with energy. Everything a thunderstorm
can do is happening all at once. Eighty-to-one-hundred-
mile-per-hour winds are carrying warm water vapor high
into the cloud, and this is being quickly transformed into
snow and rain. Descending winds from inside the cloud are
carrying down tons of pelting raindrops that are soaking
farms and towns that lie in the storm's path. Mixed with
the rain are showers of snow crystals caught in the high
reaches of the downdraft, but these will melt in lower layers
of warm air and reach the earth as raindrops. Icy hailstones
may suddenly rattle to earth in a stinging shower. To complete the stupendous show of activity the storm is putting on,
three-mile-long bolts of lightning ladder the sky, accompanied by crashing thunder.

Although hailstones often fall from a thunderstorm

downdraft. This twisting stretch of cloud is aptly named the squall line, and is a place of whirling winds. It generally does not fall very far beneath the base level of the thunderhead itself, but some meteorologists think that it can. Their theory is that one end of the roll cloud can drop to ground level and still retain its twisting motion. In this way, they believe, the destructive funnels of land tornadoes and the tornado-like "waterspouts" over the ocean are created. This seems likely, since tornadoes are always accompanied by thunderstorm activity.

The Big Anvil

Our cumulonimbus turned out to be quite a severe thunderstorm, full of sound and fury. In its mature stage, as seen in Figure C, it moved over the land, shooting great bolts of lightning and pouring down thousands of tons of rain for perhaps an hour or more. Just how long it could keep up the high pitch of its activity would depend, of course, upon how much rain material in the form of warm water vapor it could draw into its machinery from beneath its base and from the higher surrounding air. It might be assumed that this cloud was active with lightning and rain for about seventy minutes.

As it is seen in Figure E, the cloud is still manufacturing some snow and rain, but its supply of water vapor is giving out. It is growing tired because it has spent the largest part of its store of available energy, and has also used up most of its great charges of electricity in lightning bolts, although a few weak flashes can still be seen inside the cloud from

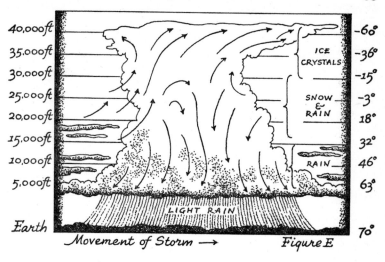

40,000ft ——————————————————— -66°
35,000ft ——————————————————— -36°
30,000ft ——————————————————— -15°
25,000ft ——————————————————— -3°
20,000ft ——————————————————— 18°
15,000ft ——————————————————— 32°
10,000ft ——————————————————— 46°
5,000ft ——————————————————— 63°
Earth ——————————————————— 70°

ICE CRYSTALS

SNOW & RAIN

RAIN

LIGHT RAIN

Movement of Storm ——→   *Figure E*

time to time. A rather moderate rain falls from almost all of the base of the cloud, and only a mild downdraft blows its cool breath over the earth beneath. What little updraft there is ascends in the rear of the cloud, and this may rise to level out and lose its force in the high atmosphere. One might say that the updraft and downdraft together represent the life-blood of a thunderstorm. When these weaken, the storm loses its vitality.

The high top of the cloud, which is entirely composed of ice crystals, has flattened out in the shape of a blacksmith's anvil. This peculiar anvil top is in reality a sign that a thunderstorm has about reached the final stage of its activity. Here, at a little over 40,000 feet, the crown is thinning into cirrus-like veils which are blown horizontally by high prevailing winds.

In another twenty or thirty minutes perhaps, the aging thunderstorm will noticeably begin to fall apart. Then the towering cloud with all its weathermaking machinery will lose completely its familiar form and shape. Either its disintegrating masses of cloud droplets will drift away into the surrounding atmosphere and evaporate, or, as often happens, the once dense cloud material will stretch out over the sky in layers of stratus cloud that can send down a fine drizzle for an hour or more.

Figure F ← 25 to 30 miles or more in extent →

For reasons of simplicity and clarity, this thunderstorm has been diagramed as a single cloud, or a "cell" of cloud activity. It is not unusual, however, to find two, three, or sometimes more cells moving along arm in arm, so to speak, as they are pictured in Figure F. They would seem at first glance to be one great cloud mass, but actually there are three active clouds, separated by what might be described as partitions of churning cloud droplets. These gusty "walls" may be two or three miles thick. Each cloud contains a thunderstorm cell operating its own machinery of updraft and downdraft, and manufacturing its individual supplies of snow, rain, hail, and lightning. You have probably experienced such a storm at one time or another. This is what happens:

The first cell of the storm darkens the sky, pours down its windy rain, accompanied by lightning and thunder, for five to ten minutes. Then the rain suddenly slackens, and may almost stop for five minutes or so. Thunder rumbles overhead meanwhile and seems to come from almost every direction. Soon gusty winds begin to blow again, after the calm, as the second cell moves in. Large raindrops splash down and in a few seconds it is raining "cats and dogs," just as it did before. A many-celled thunderstorm, if it is moving in your direction, can keep you indoors most of the afternoon. And no wonder! A large group of "local" thunderstorms can cover as much as two hundred square miles.

The Three Thunderstorm Types

The thunderstorms under discussion are of a type called "air-mass" by weathermen when they wish to describe the electrical storms that occur in our temperate climate during the summertime, or that take place in the hot tropics. These air-mass thunderstorms, as we have seen, are created when masses of moist air close to the earth are heated and become light enough to rise high into the atmosphere and develop into cumulonimbus clouds with all their stormy energy. But thunderstorm clouds can be created in two other ways.

Summer thunderstorms are ordinarily called "local," because they can build up over spots in Maine or Kansas, Ohio or Florida. In other words, they appear when local

atmospheric conditions are favorable for the making of
thunderstorms, and they are not in any sense connected with
large storm systems that move eastward over the continent.
The thunderstorm diagramed in Figure G is a quite different
kind from a local storm. Weathermen call it a "frontal"
thunderstorm, and it is a type that appears most often in
late fall, during the winter, or in early spring.

Figure G   ← 90 to 100 *miles in extent* →

The frontal thunderstorm is part of one of the great
weather disturbances or storms that sweep in a wide path
across the country from west to east. These large, rapidly
moving storm systems may spill rain or snow from the
Rocky Mountains to the Atlantic Ocean.

As the storm moves along, it is followed by an immense
dome, or "front" of cold, rather dry air. This bulge of air
pushing along the surface of the earth acts like a blunt
wedge. It keeps lifting into the atmosphere the warmer moist
air just ahead of it. If the cold wedge is moving rapidly, at
perhaps thirty-five miles an hour, the warm, moist air is
tossed high aloft where it condenses into huge cumulus

clouds that, more often than not, quickly grow into thunder-storms.

A cold front may extend its length for hundreds of miles across the United States in a line running from northeast to southwest. All along this line a great number of thunder-storms are formed and progress through their life cycles, only to be replaced by new cumulonimbus clouds. For some fifty to ninety miles just ahead of the advancing dome of the cold front, the clouds create that belt of activity called the "squall line." In this region the most violent of all elec-trical storms take place. They can be active day and night, since the extensive storm system of which they are a part takes several days and nights to cross the continent. And during its journey, the squall line maintains a fairly per-sistent and severe bluster of strong winds, rain, and light-ning.

It is no wonder that aircraft pilots dread meeting one of these squall lines, especially at night, when visibility is practically zero. They know that they must avoid the storms in one way or another, because to fly through or even be-tween them is to invite disaster. Most aircraft accidents due to stormy weather have happened because a pilot thought he could fight his way through the maze of a squall line.

When you see lightning and hear thunder in winter it seems out of place and weird, since you are accustomed to associating thunderstorms with summer. If you should ask your grandfather about it, he would most likely tell you that a winter thunderstorm is a sign that the weather will turn much colder. And this is not just a superstition; he has found by experience that it usually does happen. If he is an old "weather buff," he will no doubt explain that winter thunderstorms are created by the lifting action of an approaching mass of cold, dry air, and that, after the rain and thunder have passed, the cold air will move in with clear skies and brisk frosty days.

WEST   *Figure H*   EAST

In regions of high mountain chains like those of the Rockies, thunderstorms are initiated in still a third way, which is pictured in Figure H. Moist air, carried on prevailing westerly winds over level land, suddenly strikes the steep slopes of mountains. It flows up the slanting surfaces, and the sun-heated rock warms the ascending air, which becomes light and balloon-like and consequently soars high into the atmosphere. Here the familiar expansion, cooling, and condensation of water vapor into cloud droplets take place.

Towering cumulus clouds form and move off with the eastward-blowing winds. Many of these clouds develop strong updrafts and eventually grow into active thunderstorms that will vent their rains and lightning on mountain and valley regions as they wend their way to the east. Such thunderstorms are defined as "orographical," from the word "orography," which is the branch of physical geography that deals with mountains.

When air is lifted by mountains to produce thunderstorms, the mountains really act as "permanent fronts." For this reason thunderstorm conditions can prevail for long periods of time in certain mountainous regions.

3. THE INSIDE STORY

With Glider and Plane

Scientists have often come to remarkably good conclusions about what goes on in clouds high above the earth by working through observation and reasoning, and by applying known physical laws to their investigations. Setting up experiments in the laboratory to prove their theories has, in many instances, been helpful. To study the habits of water vapor and ice and snow at ground level, however, does not give a fully satisfactory picture of what must happen in the clouds themselves. How frustrating it must have been to the scientists of a half-century or more ago not to be able to climb up into the cloudy atmosphere for a close look at what nature was doing.

Meteorologists began to have their wish for a closer view granted with the invention of the airplane. Men at last could fly high above the earth like curious birds. As planes became stronger and more powerful, scientists, equipped with supplies of oxygen to breathe in the thin air of the high stratosphere, could actually roam the skies. They could carry with them instruments for determining temperatures, water content, barometric pressure, and other needed facts about the cloud levels they flew through. Through such investigation they added tremendously to our knowledge of weather and the atmosphere. Nevertheless, there is still more to learn. Nature's secrets are not easy to unlock.

Among the many implements meteorologists have used in their experiments are high-flying weather balloons, called radiosondes, which carry instruments that radio information back to earth. Radar, too, has become a valuable tool for the meteorologist. This electronic device, first used in World War II for spotting enemy aircraft and warships, is used by weathermen for locating thunderstorms and tornadoes, as well as for discovering more about their habits and structure. A radar beam reflected from a thunderstorm, for example, will show on the screen something of what is taking place in the storm cloud. Areas of the cloud where rain and hail are being produced appear as quite distinct patterns on the screen of a radarscope.

During 1946 and 1947, the United States Weather Bureau used both airplanes and radar to study thunderstorms in Ohio and Florida. The specially trained pilots, who made hundreds of flights through active thunderstorms at various levels, not only brought back a great deal of valuable information about the stormy insides of the clouds, but had some hair-raising adventures as well—as, during World War II, did the Army Air Force pilots, who sometimes had no choice but to fly into thunderheads during bombing missions and reconnaissance flights. Not a few commercial airline pilots learned the hard way about the brute strength and wild temper of thunderclouds by either foolishly attempting to cut through or under them or accidentally running afoul of a storm at night.

Flying inside a thunderhead is like navigating in a fog "as thick as pea soup." But with modern flying instruments to guide the pilot, the pea soup need not present difficulties. It is the "weather" inside the cloud that causes all the trouble. To encounter whirling masses of air several hundred feet in diameter, called "gusts," will cause a plane suddenly to roll and twist, and pitch forward or backward, as if a great unseen hand were shoving it around. The worst of such "bumps" and "jolts" occur in a mature thunderstorm at between five thousand and ten thousand feet up.

By running into a strong updraft three to four miles wide, where the wind current is racing at seventy miles per hour, a pilot and his plane may be carried two to three thousand feet "upstairs" in the cloud in a matter of seconds. Downdrafts are never as powerful as updrafts. Nevertheless, they have been known to sweep a plane downward for distances of as much as fifteen hundred to two thousand feet at about twenty feet a second. And flying through a downpouring curtain of rain in the downdraft beneath the base of a thunder cloud can force a plane dangerously close to the ground.

All through an active cumulonimbus cloud a pilot is sure to meet storms within the storm. At 21,000 feet he may be buffeted by a swirling snowstorm, while at about 15,000 feet he may find himself in a squall of snow and rain mixed together. Speeding hailstones the size of walnuts may hammer the plane from below or above and cause serious damage. Above the freezing level in the cloud, ice formed by fast-freezing cloud droplets or rain can coat the surfaces of the plane so heavily as to put it out of control.

Snow and ice crystals, and even raindrops, rubbing and bouncing over the metal skin of the plane, can charge it heavily with static electricity. As the electric tension mounts, the electricity discharges itself from the plane in spectacular displays of Saint Elmo's fire. Sometimes blue streamers of fiery electrical discharge shoot upward from propeller and wing tips for ten or fifteen feet. Other portions of the plane, such as engine housings and windshields, glow all over with a wavering light.

This generated electrical charge on the plane often acts to strengthen the electrical field of the cloud in the neighborhood of the plane. The resulting lightning discharge may, in this case, use the plane as a part of the conducting path. At other times, even though the plane is not strongly charged, it can connect with a streamer of lightning. Generally speaking, planes are most apt to be struck when they are in what is known as the "lightning hearth" region of the cloud—an area that lies between 15,000 and 20,000 feet, where the temperature varies from freezing to 15 degrees. Although lightning strikes on a plane often do no more than blind the pilot for a few seconds and scare the wits out of him, they can do considerable damage to electrical equipment and exposed control surfaces.

Bud Slocum's Story

Aircraft pilots are not usually very talkative people, nor are they particularly given to telling tall tales. If you are lucky enough to coax a seasoned airman to tell a few of his adventures with weather, however, the power and turmoil of thundery skies become awesome and very real.

One summer afternoon, a pilot we shall call Bud Slocum was sitting in a hangar, waiting for a crew to fuel and service his plane. He had flown many sorts of aircraft, from Army bombers and "flying boxcars" and airline ships to "flivvers." Now he was employed as the skipper of a twin-engine craft for a large manufacturing concern. The low roll of thunder from a towering white cloud not too far away seemed to remind him of thundery weather he had battled in years gone by.

"No thunderstorm is a good thunderstorm," he said, as we listened, hoping this was an introduction to a thriller. "They're the best thing in the world to stay away from with a plane. I remember coming back from a mission over Germany during the war with six enemy fighters on our tail and a great big thunderhead right ahead of us.

"There wasn't any choice to be made, so I plowed into the cloud, hoping it would be a mild one. I couldn't see if it was raining below because of the deck of shelf clouds that always jut out from a thunderhead. If it wasn't pouring down below, it was sure raining inside the cloud—wrong side up and every which way. The old bomber rolled and yawed like a drunken mule in a hurricane. Hail rattled on the cockpit canopy like gravel from a dump truck. Lightning hit us once, but fortunately did not burn up any of our electrical equipment. I was never so glad to see the sun in my life as when we finally broke through the far side of that cloud.

"I don't believe it scared me half as much, though, as a storm I got mixed up with over Montana when I was flying commercial. That was a dilly. We were on a flight from Billings to Butte when we ran into this foul-looking stack of cloud somewhere in the vicinity of Livingston. There was a six-thousand-foot dark, ragged ceiling, and the rain was so heavy that it would have been dangerous to try to go through it. I remember that Harry Taylor was my copilot, and we decided to pull up and go through at ten thousand feet, where it didn't look particularly dark or heavy, and we were pretty sure that if we did have to pull into the overcast we wouldn't get into any undue trouble.

"That's what *we* thought! Never gamble on anything that even looks like a thunderstorm. We had no sooner reached the vicinity of the front of the overcast than the ship hit a violent updraft and practically went out of control. It was all I could do to keep her right side up. Everything that wasn't fastened down began flying all over the cabin, and we didn't know what would hit us next. I finally managed to make a hundred-and-eighty-degree turn, completely throttled back, when I happened to look at the altimeter. We'd been shot aloft four thousand feet! Harry and I decided we'd had enough. The storm was probably too extensive to fly around anyway.

"We were still in the cloud and I was heading the ship back in the direction of Billings when somebody set off about a ton of TNT. A bolt of lightning struck somewhere behind the cockpit toward the tail. I couldn't see anything but light and pinwheels for about a minute. The plane was still doing all right, and we finally came out of the cloud into pretty free daylight. Harry tried to use our radio transmitter but it was dead. We dropped a spare antenna on the way back to Billings, but that didn't do us any good either.

"When we set down on the field at Billings, we had the ship checked. The radio mechanic told us that the antenna had been burned off. The jump gap was fused together, and about a two-inch hole had been burned in the top of the transmitter. As if that wasn't enough, we discovered that the inside of the transmitter looked as if someone had used a welding torch on the equipment. The funny thing was, Harry and I both wore our earphones all during the flight. It's a wonder we didn't get our ears blasted off. But you can never tell about electrical storms—except to tell yourself to stay out of them!"

It is one thing to ride a plane inside a thunderhead, but quite another to have to bail out from a plane and fall through an active cumulonimbus from top to bottom. In mid-August of 1959, the engine of Lieutenant Colonel William Rankin's F-8U Crusader jet fighter suddenly went dead at 46,000 feet—about 9 miles above the Carolina coast. The incident would not have been so serious if the Crusader had been anywhere but squarely over the uninviting anvil top of a thunderstorm. As the powerless plane plunged into the sea of cloud, Rankin made a wise decision and pulled his ejection handles. The plastic canopy of the craft shot upward and, once free of the cockpit seat, Marine Rankin found himself alone in the riotous machinery of the storm at about 40,000 feet with only his helmet, oxygen mask, and parachute pack to comfort him.

The air was burning cold at 60 degrees below zero. It seemed an age that he fell through the cloud, drenched by heavy waves of rain and blinded by flash after flash of lightning. The thunder he does not remember hearing, but recalled that he felt its concussions in his body. An automatic release opened his parachute, a treacherous object to be harnessed to in the roaring winds of a thunderstorm. At sickening speed Rankin was dragged upward and downward, 5000 feet at a stretch, through hail, snow, and rain, which pelted him as if it were borne on blasts of compressed air. At one time the fabric of his chute covered him like a collapsed tent; but he fought free, and at last came down into warmer and quieter air.

Finally he fell from the base of the cloud at 550 feet and was caught in a rush of gusty winds that dashed him across fields and into a tree. From there he was able to make his way to a nearby road, where a passing motorist rescued him and got him to a hospital. Rankin's escape from his long and turbulent adventure is unique, even for a seasoned pilot with a hundred battle missions and a jump into antiaircraft fire over Korea to his credit. Miraculously, he suffered nothing worse than shock and frostburn. But his tale of a forty-minute descent in the blustering and lightning-lit shafts of a thunderstorm will be long remembered in the ready-rooms of the flying Marines.

Balloons and Blimps

Man's first successful attempt to travel in the atmosphere above the earth was in a balloon filled with hot air, which, being lighter than the surrounding air, caused the balloon to rise. If the bag was large and buoyant enough, it could lift a man suspended beneath the balloon in a big basket slung from ropes. As the hot air cooled, however, the balloon would slowly sink to earth.

With the discovery, by the British chemist and physicist Henry Cavendish in 1766, that hydrogen gas was at least seven times lighter than atmospheric air, traveling above the earth became more practical. By 1785 men were making short and somewhat haphazard flights in baskets hung beneath varnished silk bags inflated with hydrogen. But it was not until one hundred and twenty-five years later that the balloon in a much changed form provided the first commercial flights.

From 1910 to the 1930s German, French, American, and British inventors vied with one another in developing the airship. This bulky type of craft was actually a very large cigar-shaped balloon, stiffened with a framework of aluminum, and filled with hydrogen or helium gas. Propellers driven by gasoline engines furnished the motive power, and rudders and stabilizers made accurate navigation possible. Passengers and crew rode in cabins slung under the great bag of gas.

While a few are still used in the Navy for special purposes, the airship, or dirigible, as a means of travel has joined the ghosts of the many-masted clipper ships of the sea and the proud iron horses of the railroads. The sleek heavier-than-air planes—the helicopter, the turboprop, and the jet—have pushed the lighter-than-air transports out of the skies. But the old Zeppelins had their adventures with stormy weather as they flew the airways around the earth.

The skipper of a German Navy Zeppelin tells of being forced into the cloud of a thunderstorm. "The craft rolled and bobbed like a cork on a stormy ocean," he said. "At one moment we were pushed down so low that the earth was a frightening six hundred feet below the cabin. The next moment we were carried up a gigantic stream of wind to six thousand feet, with Saint Elmo's fire streaming like forked fingers from every point of the ship. At times I thought the hull of the ship might snap in two, and we would fall to earth in twisted pieces."

A famous British airship known as the R100 also came close to destruction in a thunderstorm. She was a big ship. The balloon was 709 feet long, with a diameter of 133 feet. It required 5 million cubic feet of hydrogen to fill the hull. Five gasoline engines gave her a cruising speed of almost 60 miles an hour. During July and August of 1930, the R100, with a crew of thirty-six and seven passengers, made a flight from England to Canada.

Everything went well on the trip until the ship ran under a low, dark overcast in the vicinity of Quebec. Perhaps the pilot could not see very far aloft from the cabin under the hull, or else a long shelf of cloud hid the towering cumulonimbus above. In any event, the men aboard the R100 were soon awakened to the fact that they had run afoul of a severe thunderstorm. Quite suddenly forty-three stomachs experienced a queer sensation as the ship was lifted from 1200 feet to 4500 feet at 50 miles an hour, very much as if it had been swept upward in a fast passenger elevator. At 4500 feet the craft ceased to rise, and the pilot gained control, in spite of the tons of rain that swept over the hull from every direction. It was a wiser and very thankful crew that finally landed in Montreal.

Gliders Invade the Storm Cloud

The type of engineless plane known as a glider depends, once it is in the air, upon natural currents in the atmosphere to keep it flying. Gliders are usually towed by a powered plane until they have gained speed and altitude, and then are released to sail alone. How long a glider can remain in the air depends largely upon the skill of the pilot in using the lift of rising air streams and other winds aloft. Although gliders are employed by the Weather Bureau for meteorological investigations, and by private individuals in the United States for other purposes, sailplaning here has never been the popular sport it is in Europe. In Britain and on the Continent, numerous glider enthusiasts belong to clubs which hold exhibition meets from time to time.

Just before the Second World War, there was a final gala meeting of a German glider society in the Rhön Mountains. Mountainous country that drops away to flatlands below is a favorite location for the activities of glider sportsmen. Updrafts along mountain faces make launching easy from a good height, and sailing out over the plains insures a choice of safe landing places.

Among the visitors with their sleek little gliders were five daredevil young Nazi pilots. There was also a beautifully white mature thunderhead not too far away. Once they were airborne, the five reckless youths sped breezily off in their sailplanes and headed for a lark in the inviting billowy cloud with its darkening base and low ledges of ragged cumulus.

What the foolhardy pilots found inside the cloud was

anything but the exciting frolic they had anticipated. Only one of them survived to describe his adventure, which cost him three fingers and most of his face. His glider was caught in vicious upsweeping winds and was broken to splinters. He jumped into the roaring fog of the cloud top where the temperature was far below zero, and ice crystals cut his throat and lungs with every breath. He was half frozen from the bitter cold, but luckily he was thrown out of the updraft and began falling into warmer layers of the storm. Rain soaked him. Whirling hailstones slashed his body. Fortunately he was conscious enough to pull the ripcord of his parachute, and quite miraculously came to earth alive. His four companions were not so lucky. They too jumped, but the mighty updrafts carried them so high and held them so long that they literally froze to death.

One of the most vivid and detailed stories of adventure inside a thunderhead is told by a Swiss engineer, René Comte. Comte is a glider sportsman who has flown with much success in meetings in Switzerland, France, Germany, Sweden, and the United States, and knows his way around in the thermal waves of the atmosphere. For seven years he lived in South Africa, and discovered there better thermal conditions for sailplaning than in any other part of the world in which he had flown. It was during this time that he became intimately acquainted with the violent interior of a thunderhead—on December 1, 1951, to be exact.

The southern tip of Africa, like the peninsula of Florida, is a land of many thunderstorms. December is a hot summer month on the high plateau which forms most of South Africa; and it was here at Baragwanath, the sport and glider airfield near Johannesburg, that René Comte entered the South African National Gliding Championships.

At ten o'clock in the morning, as Comte assembled his Moswey IV glider, thick cumulus clouds were building up in the deep blue sky over the sun-drenched countryside. It was noon when he finally stepped into the rubber-cushioned cockpit of the glider, slipped the Plexiglas canopy in place, and signaled for a take-off. Towed by a small single-engine plane, he soon reached an altitude of 1200 feet over the plateau and released the tow line. If he were lucky in riding the air currents he might reach the town of Bloemfontein, 200 miles away.

From the cockpit he observed that all the cumulus clouds to the south and southeast had developed into thunderheads. In fact, the entire sky in that direction was solid with cloud, as if a front was moving in. To the north, in the direction of Bloemfontein, the sky, which had looked fairly clear at take-off, now seemed murky and menacing. Nevertheless, Comte climbed almost to cloud base on a medium-strong thermal current.

Hopping from one little cloud to another, he made his way toward the highest thing in the sky—a towering cumulonimbus about ten miles from the airfield. He knew that it would contain powerful updrafts. If he could employ them to gain high altitude he would be able to stay in the air for a longer time, and therefore have a better chance of coasting down to Bloemfontein. For this performance he stood a good chance of earning at least two diamonds of the coveted three-diamond badge, one of the trophies awarded to glider pilots by international convention: one diamond for a flight of 183 miles to a predetermined goal, and the second for a gain of altitude in free flight of more than 16,700 feet.

As he approached the magnificent white thundercloud Comte saw torrents of rain pouring from its dark underside. Bolts of lightning flashed and glowed in the boiling top. Then he sailed into the forbidding shadows under the base of the cloud, close to the falling rain, where he expected to encounter the lift of an updraft. He was not disappointed. The green ball of the indicator rose, showing about 10 feet of climb per second. Quickly switching on his electrically driven gyro-horizon, an instrument that tells a pilot when he is right side up in relation to the surface of the earth, he set the controls of the glider so that it spiraled upward in wide circles with the rising current of wind.

The air was quite smooth at first in the dark fog of the cloud, but soon became gusty as rain splashed heavily upon the cockpit canopy. In a few minutes, the Moswey IV entered the icing zone of the storm. Here, at 11,000 feet, hailstones lashed noisily and angrily at the fuselage and wings.

"The climbing speed increased gradually," Comte said in describing his experience, "and when I passed 18,000 feet I put on my oxygen mask. Before connecting the tube I squeezed it together to be sure the mask did not leak. To my utter surprise, it did leak! In spite of all my efforts I could not adjust it to my face properly. Someone had changed the strap setting, and I had forgotten to check that before take-off. So for the next forty minutes I was forced to hold the mask in place with my left hand."

It was a happy moment for René Comte when his little plane passed 24,000 feet. He knew that his first diamond was assured. The climbing speed was now 25 feet per second; and, although the air was strongly gusty, it was not difficult to keep the craft under control. The hail, however, increased, and the noise of its hammering on the Plexiglas canopy was deafening. "It scared me quite a bit," Comte remembers. "I thought of the story of the German pilots who had flown into a thunderstorm, and whose canopies had been smashed to pieces by hail. So I opened the little window and carefully put my hand outside and caught a few stones. They were the size of peas and I felt relieved. It was only that they fell so thickly that created the awful noise."

Shortly after that, Comte glanced at his altimeter. It registered 30,000 feet above sea level. Both variometers stood at the upper end of the scale, which meant that the glider was climbing at about 50 feet per second. Even though the nose of the sailplane was pointed down, it was rushing up into the cloud faster and faster—"like a man moving upstairs while strolling slowly downward on a racing escalator." The thermometer registered an outside temperature of nearly 40 degrees below zero, although the interior of the cockpit was a comfortable 45 degrees above.

At 32,000 feet the hail all but disappeared. The mists of the cloud thinned out to a milky blue, and faint sunlight shone through. Comte was just entertaining the interesting thought that he must be almost in the very top of the thunderhead, when he was enveloped by a blindingly brilliant flash. The whole cloud seemed to explode in a blaze of light as lightning hit the top of his head a sharp blow and ran through his hands into the control stick. The electrical shock, while it was not stunning, was anything but pleasant, and

Comte decided to leave the cloud as quickly as possible, "before the lightning strokes became a real nuisance."

Looking at his compass, Comte leveled out and set his craft on the course for Bloemfontein. He escaped from the thick lather of the cloud and came out into sunlight, but he could not see very far ahead. In front of him was a high, misty overcast, no doubt streaming layers of false cirrus that formed part of the anvil top of the cloud. As he flew blind in the interminable fog, the plane hit light updrafts and very strong downdrafts, smooth air, rain, then buffeting gusts again.

It seemed an eternity, watching the altimeter come down slowly turn by turn. Then, suddenly, Comte sighted the earth 6000 feet below him. He had come out under the cloud base, and was directly above the railway line that ran from Johannesburg to Kroonstad, 65 miles from the spot where he had begun his wildly soaring journey.

For an hour and a half he flew around the wall of thunderstorms that appeared to encircle him. He struggled in turbulent lifts, trying to get around the rainy areas, eagerly seeking an opening between the thunderheads through which he might find a way to his objective at Bloemfontein. But conditions seemed to be growing worse instead of better. All Comte could do was to spiral down to a landing about eleven miles south of the town of Vredefort. He had been in the air close to three hours.

Four weeks later, on December 30, Comte soared quite uneventfully, relatively speaking, into another cumulonimbus, and reached an altitude of 36,000 feet. That record still stands as the top achievement in glider flying in thermal cloud conditions. The average climbing speed at the top of the cloud was about 50 feet per second; but, at one point, Comte and his Moswey IV were lifted 700 feet in six seconds, or about 117 feet per second! And that in a blinding snowstorm that reminded him of winter in his native Switzerland, while South Africa beneath him sweltered in the heat of summer. One can expect almost anything in the tumultuous regions of a roaring thunder machine.

4. FROM AMBER TO LIGHTNING

The Beginnings of a New Science

The nature of one of the most powerful and spectacular forces in the thunderhead, lightning, was not grasped until a long series of discoveries over a period of centuries had taken place.

Five hundred years ago most people had quite a different view of the universe from that we enjoy today. Whatever they could not understand or explain was immediately assigned to a category of the mysterious and the supernatural. That the universe behaved according to natural laws instead of a kind of magic was difficult for them to comprehend. Since they were thus hampered, it is not difficult to imagine what a slow and gradual process it was for men to learn that nature, besides ruling the massive earth, the cloudy sky, and the sun and stars, also worked minutely with a complex lot of substances called matter.

That all this matter was composed of invisible particles known as atoms and molecules must have further astonished people, as scientists announced their findings. And in quite recent times men had to accept another and even stranger idea in the form of electrical charges.

The common conception of electricity is that of a flowing force which lights homes, turns the motors of refrigerators and vacuum cleaners, heats the elements of the kitchen stove, or brings to life radio and television sets. But there are also other exhibitions of electrical energy. A toy horseshoe magnet produces a type of electrical force. The sparks that sometimes pass from our fingers to some metal object, or the "crackling" of our hair when we comb it on a dry, cold day in winter, are due to discharges of electricity. Even the red glow of a poker heated in a fire is caused by "excited" atoms of iron as they give off electrical energy. Our nervous system and brain function as they do because of weak electrical currents.

The ancient Greeks prized very highly a substance called amber which they dug from the earth around the Baltic Sea. They had no idea of what it might be, but were delightfully mystified at sometimes finding the quite perfect bodies of insects imbedded in chunks of it, and they made beads and jewelry from the hard, pale yellow, rather transparent material. Later it was recognized that amber is the fossilized sap or resin from a type of pine tree that flourished perhaps fifty million years ago.

Many important discoveries are purely accidental. On a day about twenty-five hundred years ago, a famous Greek philosopher called Thales of Miletus happened to be polishing a lump of amber with a piece of woolen cloth. Noticing that lint from the cloth stuck like bristles to the surface of the yellow substance, he was curious enough about this peculiar happening to test it further. He found that his rubbed piece of amber would pick up all sorts of small, light objects such as bits of dry leaf and grass blades. Wisps of wool actually seemed to leap toward the amber. Of course, he had no notion that he was working with charges of static electricity, which is electricity at rest.

William Gilbert

Thales, influenced by the superstitious thinking of his age, assumed that amber reacted magically because a god resided in it. Not so was the opinion of William Gilbert, who was the personal physician of Queen Elizabeth I of England. About the year 1575, Gilbert, often spoken of as the father of electrical science, also tested the properties of amber by rubbing it with wool or fur. He noted its power of attracting light objects, and called this power electricity, from the Greek word for amber, which is *elektron*. "Amber indeed has a life of its own—*vis electrica*," he is said to have remarked when he was conducting an experiment for some friends. The word "electricity" remains to this day as a name for the energy that exists in all matter in the universe.

William Gilbert found that substances other than amber were also electric in nature. Jet, a shiny black mineral related to coal, and lumps of sulphur, which he called "brimstone," could be rubbed so that they behaved electrically. He made a clever little instrument that would show the presence of an electrical charge in various substances. It was a crude kind of electroscope, consisting of a light metal needle that could swing freely on a pivot like the needle of a compass. When he had rubbed different materials, he would test their attraction on the swinging needle.

In this way he found that substances divided themselves into two classes. Things like sulphur, sealing wax, amber, and glass attracted the needle after they had been rubbed. He called these "electrics." Substances like silver and copper, when rubbed, had no power to move the needle. These he called "non-electrics." Gilbert was not able to see the full meaning of his discovery as later experimenters did. His non-electrics are substances we call conductors; that is, electricity passes easily through them, as it does through copper power lines. His electrics, such as glass and amber, we now call insulators. While they can store up charges of electricity, the electrical energy cannot run freely through them. Not knowing this, Gilbert did not insulate his little electroscope, and so was never able to observe the repulsion of electrical charges.

Gilbert died in 1603, the same year in which the great Queen Elizabeth was buried in Westminster Abbey. Her court physician had laid the foundation of the science of electricity, which many men after him were to develop. It may seem strange to us that Gilbert had not wondered whether bolts of lightning were not related in some way to his *vis electrica*. But it must be remembered that Gilbert's experiments dealt with very weak electrical charges, and it is likely that he could not even begin to imagine any connection between these tiny charges and the shattering power of lightning, or to picture in his mind that vast electrical charges could be generated by such things as clouds.

It fell to a German lawyer, Otto von Guericke, to produce larger charges of electricity with which to experiment. In 1672 he cast a sphere of sulphur about seven or eight inches in diameter, fitted it with an axle and crank, and thereby invented the first machine for the generation of electricity. By means of the crank he could turn the ball of sulphur briskly with one hand while he rubbed it with the other. This procedure gave the sulphur quite a vigorous charge. Small objects such as feathers and bits of paper would leap about in the most amazing fashion between the sulphur and the floor, as the electricity on the sphere alternately repelled or attracted them. Isaac Newton, who established the laws of mechanical motion, a few years later performed a similar experiment with a revolving glass sphere rubbed with a piece of silk cloth.

Von Guericke soon found that the electricity on his sphere of sulphur could be passed over to other objects by conduction. Electricity from the charged ball would travel along a yard or more of linen thread to attract scraps of paper or straw at the far end. He found, too, that cranking and rubbing his sulphur ball in a totally dark room produced a dim, bluish light. Faint and unspectacular as it must have been, the light von Guericke saw was actually a small discharge of Saint Elmo's fire.

The actions of the feathers and fragments of paper and straw in the presence of his electric generator were certainly amusing and intriguing. Von Guericke, however, could not explain why these objects were sometimes attracted and sometimes were repulsed or driven away. It was about sixty years later that a Frenchman with a rather long name evolved an interesting explanation.

Positive and Negative Electricity

Charles François de Cisternay Du Fay was one of the many talented and ingenious men whom King Louis XIV gathered together at his court in the seventeenth century. In the halls of the new Académie des Sciences, which the king had founded in 1666, there was much discussion about electricity, although no one seemed to have much knowledge of it. People in general looked to the blossoming sciences for the invention of practical and useful things. There must be some use for this electricity, they said, or why is everyone making so much fuss about it?

Du Fay decided he would investigate that—and more! He already knew of the discovery of William Gilbert's electrics and non-electrics, and of von Guericke's experiments with conducting electricity from one object to another. Starting from there, he set up a sort of laboratory at Versailles where he could build friction machines to his heart's content and work with all sorts of substances.

Thus Du Fay discovered for himself the effects of electrical attraction and repulsion that von Guericke had noticed. He came to the conclusion that electricity must be a kind of invisible fluid, because it could flow from one object to another. He was also convinced that there were two kinds of this fluid, and that all substances normally contained both kinds. Since these two kinds of electricity were usually present in equal quantities, they neutralized one another. To distinguish between them he called them *positive* and *negative* electricity.

He further reasoned that with a friction machine the two kinds of electricity could be separated one from the other, and then they would attract and neutralize each other if they were of different kinds, and repel each other if they were of the same kind. He was quite right in this, of course, but he does not seem to have settled upon a precise definition as to which was positive and which was negative. Actually, as far as names are concerned, it makes little difference which kind of electricity is given the label of positive, but the designation that was used in Benjamin Franklin's day has persisted. As Franklin did, we say that amber, rubber, sealing wax, or sulphur rubbed with wool exhibits a negative charge; while glass rubbed with silk shows a positive charge.

Charles Du Fay, as well as a few other scientists of his day, had come to the important conclusion that there was electricity in everything in the universe. The fluid of electricity was not restricted to just a few objects, but was a common property of such everyday things as houses and trees, the earth, and even animals and men. And again he was right. Nevertheless, Du Fay does not seem to have brought electrified clouds and lightning into his speculations about electricity, any more than Gilbert did.

It was Isaac Newton, who lived at the same time as Du Fay, who expressed an opinion that lightning must be composed of electric fluid, although he apparently could offer no explanation of how so vaporous and impermanent a thing as a cloud might function as a friction machine capable of generating electricity.

By the middle of the 1700s electricity had become quite a common topic of conversation and source of interest. Lectures and public shows demonstrating what could be done with electric-friction machines drew large crowds of curious spectators, especially in Germany and Holland. And in quiet laboratories men of science were devising all kinds of experiments in an effort to explain the habits and nature of the strange force they called electrical fluid.

Storing Electricity

One of the most helpful and important discoveries to come from eighteenth-century experimentation was the electric bottle, or, as we know it, the Leyden jar. It had previously been demonstrated that electricity could be led from one object to another by using some sort of conducting material to connect the two. Now it was found that a quantity of electricity could be stored for a time in a special form of container and discharged from there at will.

Two men invented the storage bottle quite independently in 1745 and 1746: Ewald von Kleist of Pomerania in Prussia, and Pieter van Musschenbroek of Leyden, Holland. Since van Musschenbroek was much better known than Kleist, the invention rather naturally was named for the Dutch city of Leyden.

The Leyden jar consisted of a wide-mouthed bottle, not

unlike the familiar pint jar used for canning. The inside of the jar was lined about two-thirds of the way up with thin silver foil (which was known to be a conductor of electricity), and the outside was similarly wrapped with the same material. The jar was closed with a wooden cap through which ran a copper or brass rod that touched the foil in the bottom of the jar. The top of the rod terminated in a small sphere of metal to prevent possible leakage of the electrical fluid from the foil inside the jar. When the rod was connected to an active friction machine by a wire, the silver foil in the bottle was soon heavily charged with electricity. Nowadays, we would call the Leyden jar a "condenser."

What astonished experimenters with the Leyden jar was the amount of electricity that could be stored in it. Both von Kleist and van Musschenbroek had received staggering shocks when they held a wire to connect the copper rod with the outside wrapping of foil. If a finger was brought close to the tip of the rod, a vigorous spark like a miniature flash of lightning would leap across the space. The owner of the finger might receive a real jolt. Even a number of people, holding hands, would receive by conduction the same shock from a discharging Leyden jar.

The Leyden jar gave the first evidence that electricity could be collected and stored in quantity. Eighteenth-century citizens immediately began enjoying the novel entertainment of being "shocked"; and some physicians even went so far as to experiment with "curing" their patients with strong doses of electricity. Beyond that, however, no one could think how this stored-up electric fluid could be put to any practical use. Nor was it yet suspected that electricity could be stored in clouds.

News of the Leyden jar eventually crossed from Europe to America in slow-traveling sailing ships. It is not difficult to guess who became one of the first of the American colonists to show great interest: a Philadelphia printer by the name of Benjamin Franklin.

In 1746 Franklin imported a friction machine from England, which can still be seen in the Franklin Institute in Philadelphia. Soon after that he acquired a whole family of Leyden jars and became an avid experimenter with electricity. A small group of friends joined Franklin in his electrical investigations, and together they formed the first scientific society in America—a diligent little organization that soon was drawing the attention of experimental scientists on the Continent of Europe.

By 1749 there was in the back of Franklin's mind an idea (and what a bold one it must have seemed to the people of his day) that lightning was really an effect of electrical conduction. If electricity could be carried along wires and pass through water and air, it seemed almost certain that lightning must be a great spark of electrical fluid somehow generated in the sky and conducted from cloud to earth. Since there should be a way to prove it, he immediately set about planning an experiment with nature's thunderous sparks.

Franklin was decidedly aware that there were many similarities between electricity in the laboratory and the great sparks from the sky. But we have only to put ourselves in his eighteenth-century shoes to realize his difficulties in trying to prove that nature's sparks and man-made electrical sparks consisted of the same form of energy. Compared to today's wealth of laboratory devices for working with electricity, Franklin's tools were few and primitive. He could produce only small charges of electricity with which to experiment, and vital knowledge of the electrical behavior of atoms was not available to scientists of his day. The best he could do was to prove by simple comparison that his little friction machines and Leyden jars were, in some mysterious way, related to nature's equipment in storm clouds. And his best was very good indeed.

But before we consider Franklin's plan, his famous kite, and his lightning rods, we should pause for a look at some of the demonstrations that nature herself provides with cloudy friction machines and heavenly Leyden jars.

5. THE HEAVENLY FRICTION MACHINE

Lightning Is Electricity!

It is a much simpler matter to attribute the workings of nature to hidden magical powers than to arrive at the truth about them through intelligent observation, reasoning, and experiment. Magic, of course, does not explain anything. The imagined gods that resided in a lump of amber and provided its mysterious power to attract bits of grass and wool had to satisfy ancient men because they had not yet learned to analyze nature and to imitate her in experiments.

Nature has been man's constant companion since his beginning. Long before he had an adequate language with which to describe and discuss what he saw in nature, weather, fair and foul, passed over the earth where he lived. Rain gave him water necessary for life, and sometimes took his life by drowning him. Winters of snow and ice both stimulated his ambitions and drove him to warm caves and huts. Thunderstorms, with their terrifying bolts of lightning, often put him in peril of his life, but benignly provided essential nitrogen for the growth of the plants and trees about him. It took him thousands of years, however, to discover the whys and wherefores of nature and to adjust himself to them. And it was a long and tedious process for man to learn to protect himself against the violent energy in nature and, eventually, to turn some of it to his own use.

Earliest man could do little but flee to some sort of shelter before a roaring storm of rain and lightning. Unseen spirits or gods, he thought, were angrily pouring out their merciless vengeance upon him. The much later men who lived in villages and cities adopted a more sophisticated method of dealing with electrical storms. Since lightning was regarded at this time as an act of God, prayer might help in diverting thunderbolts. For many centuries on the Continent of Europe and in Britain it was customary not only to pray when a thunderstorm was approaching, but also to ring church bells as loudly as possible. Picture the bell-ringers madly scrambling to get to the bell ropes in a church tower as thunder boomed ominously from an oncoming storm. Then the wild clanging of the bells would add its metallic din to the furious sound of wind and rain, and the keen crack of lightning and roll of thunder.

In proof of how popular this bell-ringing was in the face of electrical storms, many church bells dating from the eleventh, twelfth, and thirteenth centuries have a Latin inscription cast around their flaring rims: FULGUR FRANGO— "I break lightning." To the superstitious, bell-ringing tended to drive away evil spirits that rode the storm and directed the lightning; to those who possessed a very primitive notion of physics, the ringing was supposed to set up waves in the air that would interrupt the path of the thunderbolt.

Actually, all the bell-ringing did was to place the poor bell-ringers in an admirable position to be knocked dead by lightning. Even as early as the eighth century so many bell-ringers were electrocuted that Emperor Charlemagne is said to have issued a decree forbidding the ringing of church bells in times of thunderstorms. But it takes a long time for superstitious customs to fade away. Trying to dispel lightning with the clanging of bells went on for some nine hundred years.

In 1784 a book aimed at showing how perilous and useless was this ancient custom was published in Germany. The evidence it gave was startling. In Germany alone, during the course of 33 years, lightning had damaged or destroyed 386 church steeples and had killed 103 ringers who managed the bell ropes.

Germany is only one example of the destructive activity of lightning. History records an almost endless list of buildings all over Europe that suffered from the fiery darts of thunderstorms. The old church of St. Paul's in London was among the English houses of worship that received repeated lightning damage. An observer tells us that on June 4, 1561, the steeple of St. Paul's was struck. Flames of fire which broke out just beneath the great cross spread downward and burned the wooden spire to the stonework of the tower and the bell frames. In less than four hours, not only was the steeple consumed, but all the roofs of the church itself.

In Venice, Italy, the bell tower, or *campanile*, of St. Mark's stands as a veteran of lightning's fury. The original tower was constructed of wood. Between 1388 and 1489 it was twice totally destroyed by lightning. A new tower of stone, 350 feet high, was erected, but this structure, in an area of numerous thunderstorms, was no more immune to lightning than were its wooden ancestors. In the space of a century it received three damaging hits. Then in the year 1745 a powerful bolt of lightning all but wrecked it. It was repaired at considerable expense, only to be severely damaged again in 1761 and 1762. Wise authorities provided for the installation of a Franklin lightning rod in 1766, and the beautiful tower remained secure from summer skyfire.

Gunpowder and Lightning

The ringers of bells were not the only victims of lightning that found its way to church towers. During the seventeenth and eighteenth centuries small arms and cannon became important weapons in warfare. Since the storage of large supplies of gunpowder in kegs was often a problem that confronted artillery officers, they frequently solved it by using the cellars and vaults of churches as convenient magazines. That these were both spacious and protected from weather was undeniably true, but what better way to court disaster than to place explosives beneath the spire of a church during the season of thunderstorms! It is little wonder that gruesome accounts of calamities like that in Brescia at the foot of the Italian Alps have come down to us. Here, in 1769, one hundred tons of gunpowder were stored in the crypts beneath the church of St. Nazaire. Lombardy is a very thundery region in midsummer, and a typically energetic storm moved over Brescia on a fateful July afternoon. A powerful bolt of lightning from the dark cloud struck the tower of the church, passing through the metal bell-stands, shot earthward into the vaults below, and set off the gunpowder in one mighty blast. One-sixth of the city was laid in ruins, and three thousand citizens lost their lives.

It is interesting to find that there are quite a few historic buildings that have been hit by lightning perhaps on many occasions, but have received no damage because of their unusual construction. Some had roofs and spires covered with lead sheets, which were connected with the ground by metal downspouts. The towers of others were crowned by iron ornaments which were, in turn, connected in some manner to metal stairways or ladders that reached to the ground. In both cases the construction added up to effective lightning rods.

In the first century B.C. the poet-philosopher Lucretius asked himself some questions that were obviously the result of good observation and reasoning: "If it was Jupiter who sent down lightning, why should he scatter his flaming bolts in so wanton and wasteful a manner on the empty sea and on the temples dedicated to him? Why should he aim his lightning so often toward high mountains, trees, tall buildings and sculptures? And why should he wait until thick, dark clouds had covered the sky before casting his thunderbolts?" Of course steeples, towers, domes, and monuments were the highest structures in cities and towns, standing as they did well above dwellings and shops. In the country, mountains, hills, and trees reached above the level of farm, field, and plain. Yet, even in the mid-eighteenth century no one had a way of knowing that these tall objects were favorite targets for thunderbolts because lightning seeks the way of least resistance between cloud and earth. Buildings and trees present a short-cut to earth for lightning not only because they are high, but because they are better conductors than the surrounding air.

For the same reason the masts of ships at sea are targets for lightning. Any vessel on an open expanse of water rides well above the surface, a solitary and tall object which is much in the same position as a church spire thrust above the lower levels of a city. In the days of wooden ships with wooden masts, it is easy to imagine how frequent and disastrous were the strikes by lightning, especially upon vessels in the vicinity of land. The masts of sailing ships hit by lightning were invariably reduced to splintered wrecks. Rigging and timber crashed to decks, and it was not unusual for sails and tarred ropes to be set afire. In such close quarters as a ship's deck, seamen had little chance of escape from falling debris, and even from the lightning bolt itself. There were apt to be serious casualties if a ship became the victim of lightning during a severe squall.

Several records tell of the complete destruction of British and American naval vessels in the late eighteenth century when lightning found its way below decks and touched off explosions in the powder magazines. It seems strange that naval authorities and private shipowners of those days were so slow in availing themselves of the lightning conductor invented by Franklin, a device by which lightning would pass through chains or cables that led over the ship's side into the water. It was as late as 1820 before many wooden ships were protected in this manner. Of course, with the coming of iron-hulled ships and steel masts, the entire vessel became a lightning conductor. "Grounded" in the water of the sea, the iron ship served as its own lightning rod.

Franklin Plans an Experiment

The inventor of the lightning rod, Benjamin Franklin, is about as well known to us as General George Washington. Besides being a master printer, an author and philosopher of no mean ability, and an eminent statesman, he possessed the restless, adventurous mind of a scientist.

By the time he had reached the age of forty, in 1746, Franklin had a substantial income from his publishing business. He decided that he could afford to devote some time to the many things that interested him—among them, electricity. It was in 1746 that he bought from a Dr. Spence the now famous "electrical Machine," or generator of static electricity. His home in Philadelphia became his laboratory, and his patient wife, Deborah, must have been surprised, if not sometimes alarmed, to find herself living with a clutter of strange devices that whirred and crackled and spat sparks.

Franklin's friction machine consisted of a hollow glass sphere that could be revolved rapidly as it rubbed on a pad of silk. The electricity it generated was collected by a sort of metal comb from the glass, and from there was transferred by a stiff wire to the surface of an insulated brass ball. From this temporary collector the electricity could be led over another wire to one or more Leyden jars for storage. It was with such equipment as this that Franklin and his small circle of enthusiastic friends experimented with the "new" electricity, carefully recording their discoveries in notebooks which still exist today.

Franklin was familiar with Du Fay's experiments and his theories about electricity, but he had come to many con-

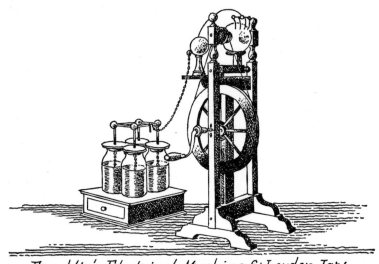

Franklin's Electrical Machine & Leyden Jars

clusions of his own. Instead of two kinds of electricity, Franklin decided there was but one kind. He argued that electricity is a "common element" which is contained in all bodies, no matter of what material they are made. If a body possessed more than its usual share of electrical fluid it was said to be plus, or positively charged. If a body had less than its normal amount, it was minus, or negatively charged.

This "single fluid" notion of electricity seemed reasonable and sound to Franklin and other scientists of his day, and was accepted by physicists for more than a hundred years. The older "two fluid" explanation proposed by Du Fay, however, seems to fit better into our modern knowledge of electricity. In any event, the terms "positive" and "negative" are still used to distinguish the separation of electrical charges.

In Franklin's day, many people still continued to hold strange ideas about what lightning might be and what caused it. Some had got no further than had the medieval scholars, who defined it as an act of God. Others said that clouds striking together caused sparks, as when flint strikes steel. Then there were a few who reversed everything and maintained that thunder was the cause of lightning. They were as confused as the citizens of the ancient world in the first century A.D., when the Roman philosopher Seneca oddly accused the Etruscan Greeks of entertaining foolish notions. "We believe that lightning arises because the clouds clash one against the other," he said. "The Etruscans think that the clouds clash so that there will be lightning." Benjamin Franklin, however, with his reasonable, scientific approach to the problem, observed striking similarities between a long flash of lightning and the short sparks from his friction machine and his Leyden jars. Although he was not the only experimenter to observe these similarities, he seemed to be alone in his determined desire to prove that they had some basis.

Franklin thought he saw twelve unmistakable resemblances between his man-made lightning and lightning from the skies: "1. Giving light 2. Color of the light 3. Crooked direction 4. Swift motion 5. Being conducted by metals 6. Crack or noise in exploding 7. Subsisting in water or ice 8. Rending bodies it passed through 9. Destroying animals 10. Melting metals 11. Firing inflammable substances 12. Sulphureous smell."

Items 11 and 9 were well demonstrated during a "party of pleasure on the banks of the Schuylkill"—what must have been a kind of electrical picnic beside the river that runs through Philadelphia. Brandy was set to flaming, and a cooking fire was kindled, both by sparks from Leyden jars. Then a turkey for the dinner was dispatched on the spot by a severe electric shock. (During a previous experiment with a chicken, Franklin had come near to electrocuting himself.)

In a letter to his friend John Lining of Charleston, South Carolina, Franklin added this thought to the list of similarities between his electrical sparks and lightning, thereby anticipating the form of his sharp-tipped lightning rods: "The electric fluid is attracted by points. We do not know whether this property is in lightning. But since they agree in all the particulars wherein we can already compare them, is it not probable that they agree likewise in this? Let the experiment be made."

It is all very well to say, "Let's get on with the job," but devising the experiment is not so simple. How would one, for instance, lure a bolt of lightning from the sky and sample it? Would it be possible to discover whether "clouds that contain lightning are electrified or not," without the experimenter's being blasted to kingdom come?

Franklin rather carefully sketched the details of a possible experiment in a paper entitled "Opinions and Conjectures, concerning the Properties and Effects of the Electrical Matter, arising from Experiments and Observations, made at Philadelphia, 1749." A copy of this paper was sent with a letter to the British Royal Society in 1750: "On the top of some high tower or steeple, place a kind of sentry-box, big enough to contain a man and an electrical stand. From the middle of the [insulated] stand let an iron rod rise and pass bending out of the door, and then upright 20 or 30 feet, pointed very sharp at the end. If the electrical stand be kept clean and dry, a man standing on it when such clouds are passing low, might be electrified and afford sparks, the rod drawing fire to him from the cloud. If any danger to the man should be apprehended (though I think there would be none), let him stand on the floor of his box, and now and then bring near to the rod the loop of a wire that has one end fastened to the leads [the grounded metal roof], he holding it by a wax handle; so the sparks, if the rod is electrified, will strike from the rod to the wire, and not affect him."

Benjamin Franklin did not proceed with the experiment as he had outlined it. There were no very high steeples in Philadelphia in 1750, and the only available one was in the process of being built. This was Christ Church, and the soaring spire would follow a design by the famous Sir Christopher Wren. With no steeple at hand, Franklin busied himself with other ideas. His letter to members of the Royal Society for Improving Natural Knowledge by Experiments, strangely enough, drew no enthusiasm. It is altogether likely that they did not grasp the significance of Franklin's plan. Even if one survived this dangerous experiment, what could be proved?

Induction and Ionization

What would happen during the experiment (as Franklin correctly supposed) is this: A thunderstorm cloud, having a strong negative charge at its base, moves near a tall, pointed metal rod, which is supported by a small wooden platform fitted with glass legs and so is insulated from the earth. The metal rod, which we will call the conductor, has on its surface a mixture of positive and negative charges. The force of the negative charge in the cloud separates the charges on the conductor, and draws a purely positive charge to the top of the rod, while, at the same time, it repels a purely negative charge to the base of the conductor, as can be seen in Figure I.

This process is known as "electric induction" and can be demonstrated simply with a horseshoe magnet, a nail, and a few small carpet tacks. Here, one pole of the magnet, without touching the nail, induces, or "brings in," similar electric

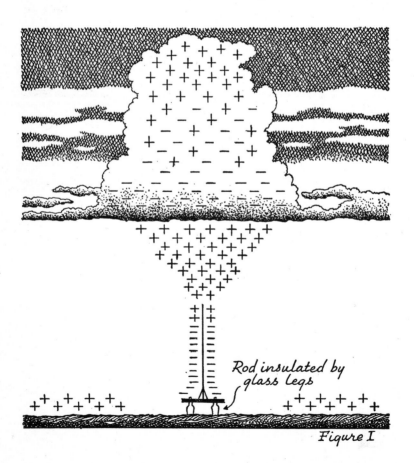

Rod insulated by glass legs

Figure I

Nail assumes negative charge

properties in the nail. The nail, in turn, acts as a magnet in attracting the positive charge on the carpet tacks, while their negative charge is repelled. In the case of the cloud, if the electric tension, or pressure, is strong enough, some of the positive charge at the top of the metal conducting rod will stream off as a faintly glowing discharge of Saint Elmo's fire, and will pass upward through the atmosphere to neutralize some of the negative charge at the base of the cloud. The electricity in this display of Saint Elmo's fire is carried aloft on atoms and molecules of gases in the air. The molecules, of course, take on an excess of positive charge, and are attracted by the negative charge at the base of the cloud. These helpful particles of matter—consisting for the most part of atoms or groups of atoms of nitrogen and oxygen—are called ions.

An atom has a tiny central bit of substance called a nucleus, and around the nucleus other particles of matter, called electrons, revolve in orbits, much as the earth revolves around the sun. Ordinarily, the entire electrical charge of each atom of matter is neutral, because the positive charge of the nucleus and the negative charges of the usual number of electrons the particular atom possesses cancel each other.

However, for various reasons, an atom can lose an electron or two, and can even pick up some extra ones. Among the many ways in which electrons can be knocked out of atoms, the simplest is by rubbing two surfaces of material together. Franklin's friction machine and your sliding, in woolen clothes, over a plastic automobile seat are both instrumental in knocking electrons out of atoms. This loss of electrons leaves an atom, or group of atoms, with an excess positive charge. Gaining electrons, on the other hand, gives the atom an excess negative charge. In either case, the atom is said to be ionized. That is, it is no longer electrically neutral but is charged either positively or negatively, as the case may be.

In a thunder cloud, the rubbing together of ice and snow crystals and the breaking up of water drops knock electrons out of atoms and consequently ionize them. And, as we shall discover later, sparks of electricity, such as lightning, also create ions in the atmosphere.

In Figure I it can be seen that the streaming upward of the positive charge on the glass-insulated conducting rod continues until the rod is left with little else but a strong negative charge. It is apparent that the rod does not actually draw electricity from the cloud, but the effect is quite the same as if it had done so.

But what happens if the tall conducting rod is *not* insulated

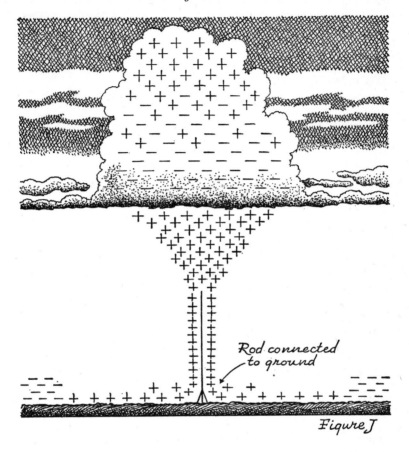

Rod connected to ground

Figure J

from the earth, or, as we commonly say, is "grounded"? The induced negative charge seen at the base of the rod in Figure I remained because it was blocked from the earth by the non-conducting glass legs of the platform. In Figure J, however, the rod is no longer insulated from the earth, and so the negative charge has been pushed far away from the base of the rod. With no negative charge to interfere, positive electricity will continue to stream upward from the rod until the cloud with its large negative charge moves away.

D'Alibard and Coffier

The contents of the paper that Franklin sent to the British Royal Society had, in the meantime, somehow come to the attention of other scientists across the Atlantic. French physicists had been reading with much interest about the variety of experiments with "electrical fluid" that were being carried on in Philadelphia by the budding American scientific group that centered around Benjamin Franklin. Franklin's proposed plan to discover whether thunder clouds were electrified especially fired the imagination of a young Frenchman by the name of d'Alibard. He decided to try the experiment himself, and without the benefit of a high steeple.

In the village of Marly, just outside of Paris, d'Alibard built a small shed with one open side. A forty-foot iron rod, secured to a wooden base that stood on four tall wine bottles for purposes of insulation, ran out the open side of the shed, then upward. To keep the rod from bending he supported it with silk ribbons between two vertical wooden poles. The rest of the equipment consisted of several yards of copper wire. One end of the wire was fastened to a metal rod driven into the ground outside the shed (instead of to a metal roof covering as Franklin had planned in his use of a steeple), while the other end was connected to a one-foot length of slender iron rod. This rod was fitted with a handle made of beeswax. The wax, being a non-conductor, would prevent anyone holding the rod from receiving an electric shock.

D'Alibard, who was too occupied with other scientific projects to wait for a thunderstorm to visit his laboratory shed, instructed a retired infantryman by the name of

Jacques Coffier in the use of the equipment, and stationed him in the shelter. On May 10, 1752, the patient Coffier watched the sky darken as a thunder cloud approached. When the cloud seemed well overhead, and thunder was rolling, the old soldier entered the shed. He grasped the wax-handled rod and brought its tip near the tall iron rod that pointed skyward. He was rewarded with a crackling jet of bright sparks, as positive electricity left the earth to flow over the grounded wire and upwards to the thunder cloud.

Everything happened just as his employer said it would. Coffier's excited shouts soon attracted the attention of nearby villagers, who came running to find out what all the fluster was about. The display of electric fireworks they viewed in the shed was most amazing. Whether or not they realized the importance of what they saw, Jacques Coffier and his friends were witnesses to the first definite proof that thunder clouds were indeed electrified. Without an electrically charged cloud overhead, Coffier would not have obtained his stream of sparks.

Franklin Makes a Kite

Because there was no radio or transatlantic telephone in 1752, Benjamin Franklin did not hear for some months of d'Alibard's success, nor did he know of his sudden fame in Europe as the author of the experiment. As a matter of fact, since no high steeple was available to him, he had evolved another plan for testing the thunder clouds. He would try to go higher than a steeple. He would use a kite!

In preparation for his experiment he constructed a sturdy

kite from a large silk handkerchief and two light ribs of
wood. On an afternoon in June 1752, a thunderstorm moved
in, and Franklin was ready. His son, then a young man of
twenty, helped to get the kite up into the air, where it soared
to a goodly height. It was anchored to a long stretch of
stout linen twine, and to the lower end of the twine Franklin tied a length of silk ribbon to hold to, so that the kite
and its string would be insulated from the ground. (Franklin himself, of course, would be connected to the ground.)
Just above the knot where the silk ribbon and the linen
twine met, Franklin had his son tie an iron key, possibly to
"attract" the electric fluid from the sky.

The kite pitched and tossed under the dark storm cloud,
and as time went by Franklin could see no evidence that
the cloud was electrified. He was quite discouraged, and
had just begun to think that his contrivance was a failure,
when he noticed that loose fibers of the linen twine began
to bristle outward and to avoid one another. Here, at least,
was evidence of an electrical charge. He touched his knuckle
to the dangling key and felt the passage of a strong spark!
It was a memorable moment for Franklin: he knew without
a doubt now that the lightning of thunderstorms and electricity were one and the same thing. He must have known,
too, that he was fortunate. A flash of lightning, using his
kite and its tether of twine as a conductor to earth, might have
fatally included him as part of the "flying lightning rod."

From this experiment, Franklin went on to discover the
sign of the electrical charge in the base of the thunderstorm
clouds, which he speaks of as "gusts," or "thunder-gusts." He
erected what amounted to a lightning rod on his house, al-

though the rod, instead of passing over the outside of the house to the ground, descended inside a stair-well as an insulated wire and was finally grounded to an iron water pump in the basement. With this apparatus he was able to charge a Leyden jar with lightning, and this he compared experimentally with the known charge from glass rubbed with silk. To make this comparison he used an electroscope consisting of a small cork ball suspended from a fine silk thread.

The experiment is described in a letter written to one of his scientific friends, Peter Collinson, in September 1753: "At last, on the 12th of *April,* 1753, there being a smart gust of some continuance, I charg'd one phial pretty well with lightning, and the other equally, as near as I could judge, with electricity from my glass globe; and, having placed them properly, I beheld, with great surprize and pleasure, the cork ball play briskly between them, and was convinced that one bottle was electrised *negatively.*

"I repeated this experiment several times during the gust, and in eight succeeding gusts, always with the same success; and being of the opinion . . . that the glass globe electrises *positively,* I concluded, that the clouds are *always* electrised *negatively,* or have always in them less than their natural quantity of the electric fluid.

"Yet notwithstanding so many experiments, it seems I concluded too soon; for at last, *June* the 6th, in a gust which continued from five o'clock, P.M., to seven, I met with one cloud that was electrised *positively,* tho' several that pass'd over my rod before, during the same gust, were in the *negative* state."

It is of interest to note, as Franklin goes on with his letter, that he discovered a positive charge in lightning from the cloud *"near the end of the gust."* From what is known now, some thunder clouds do exhibit a positive charge at their bases. As a thunderstorm assumes its mature stage, a small region of positive charge sometimes develops in the down-draft associated with heavy rain. Not having our modern store of meteorological knowledge at his disposal, Franklin could only come to the conclusion "that the clouds of a thunder-gust are most commonly in a negative state of elec-tricty, but sometimes in a positive state." He believed the latter to be rare.

Franklin's observations were correct. Scientists of today would add, however, that it is not the entire cloud but the base of the cloud which commonly holds a negative charge; and that the top of the cloud supports a positive charge.

Franklin was a practical man. He soon turned the results of his electrical experiments to the benefit of mankind. The sharp-pointed lightning rod he proposed for the protection of buildings has become a sort of trademark for his investiga-tions of electricity. In the 1753 issue of his *Poor Richard's Almanack,* he announced to the world the virtues of the lightning rod.

"It has pleased God in his Goodness to Mankind, at length to discover to them the Means of securing their Habitations and other Buildings from Mischief by Thunder and Light-ning. The Method is this: Provide a small Iron Rod (it may be made of the Rod-iron used by the Nailers) but of such Length, that one End being three or four feet in the moist Ground, the other may be six or eight Feet above the highest Part of the Building. To the upper End of the Rod fasten about a Foot of Brass Wire, the size of a common Knitting-needle, sharpened to a fine Point; the Rod may be secured to the House by a few small Staples. If the House or Barn be long, there may be a Rod and Point at each End, and a middling Wire along the Ridge from one to the other. A House thus furnished will not be damaged by Lightning, it being attracted by the Points, and passing thro the Metal into the Ground without hurting any Thing. Vessels also, having a sharp pointed Rod fix'd on the top of their Masts, with a Wire from the Foot of the Rod reaching down, round one of the Shrouds, to the Water, will not be hurt by Lightning."

Like many another invention, the lightning rod met with suspicion and criticism. It also underwent all sorts of changes at the hands of experimenters who were not as well educated in the habits of electricity as was Franklin. Most of these curious contraptions ended in failure, and sometimes disaster. But an invention so sound in principle was bound to succeed. Even in Franklin's lifetime, many buildings upon which rods were properly installed were saved from the destructive and fiery blasts of lightning. Proof today of the success of the invention is that about the only lightning damage we hear about happens to buildings that are *not* protected by lightning rods.

Up to the time of his death in 1790, at the age of eighty-four, Franklin was never quite sure whether his rod *attracted* lightning to its pointed top, or *conducted* it to the earth. It was not until the latter half of the nineteenth century that the question was finally solved, and the more intimate secrets of lightning's behavior were discovered.

6. TUNNEL IN THE SKY

The Clash of Electrical Giants

Benjamin Franklin had discovered to his great satisfaction, and demonstrated to the world, that thunderstorms are electrically charged. It must have been apparent to the ingenious Philadelphia experimenter that "thunder-gusts" were in some strange way like his electricity-producing friction machine. But how? Meteorology, or the science of weather, was not yet born. Little or nothing was known about what went on in the upper atmosphere.

Everyone certainly knew a cloud when he saw one in the sky, but no one could explain why there were different types of cloud, or what part they played in the ever-changing pattern of weather. A storm was a storm, and a thunder-gust was simply a thunder-gust, that windy electrical phenomenon of summer days and nights. Rain, snow, and hail were familiar forms of precipitation, but no one in the year 1752 had any knowledge of how they were produced in clouds, or knew much about their physical properties. Least of all could anyone—including Franklin himself—imagine in what way winds, ice and snow crystals, and hailstones worked together, as parts of a giant friction machine, to generate so vast an electrical spark as a flash of lightning.

Early experimenters, as we know, rubbed amber or other resinous substances with wool to produce an electrical charge, which they called "negative" to distinguish it from the charge they obtained by rubbing glass with silk, which they called "positive." But none of these men of centuries past got around to testing the electrical effects of a large variety of substances. And, of course, the scientific instruments of those days were few, crude, and simple compared to those at the disposal of the scientists of today.

Modern scientists can determine the amount and kind of even the tiniest electrical charge on any substance, such as a single snow crystal or a single raindrop. They know that dry ice crystals or snow crystals, rubbing along the wings and body of an airplane in flight, will produce large amounts of electricity. During the process, the surface of the plane can become so strongly charged with negative electricity that it will discharge long streams of Saint Elmo's fire, which cause so much "static" noise as to make the plane's radio useless. They also know that the particles of ice and snow that do the rubbing keep a charge of positive electricity. This bit of knowledge is important. It helps us to understand how electricity can be generated in a vast, active cumulonimbus cloud.

If a small blast of bouncing snow and ice crystals can electrically charge an airplane, consider the amount of electrical energy that cubic miles of wind-tossed ice and snow particles, rubbing against one another, can produce in the top of a thunderhead. Benjamin Franklin must have found it difficult indeed to try to picture such a powerful friction machine as this natural electric generator, manufacturing thousands of millions of volts that discharge sparks many miles in length: a machine made up solely of such unlikely materials as water and ice and wind!

The reason why a thunder cloud is so efficient a generator of enormous charges of electricity is that it contains such an infinite number of colliding ice particles and falling raindrops. Each drop and crystal itself acquires from the rubbing and colliding only a very, very small charge of electricity; but, added together, as if the charges were collected in a Leyden jar six miles in diameter and nine miles high, they represent a truly enormous quantity of electric charge.

It is entirely possible that a quite large thunder cloud might contain 150,000 tons of water in the form of raindrops and ice crystals. The total water would fill a pond 4000 feet long by 500 feet wide, and a little over 5 feet deep. In the cloud this amount of water would be divided into something over 9 million million raindrops and ice crystals. Taken together, the tiny electrical charges on all these liquid and solid particles of water amount to amazing quantities of electrical force.

A flash of lightning is actually built from countless small charges of electricity under very high tension, and it lasts for only the briefest moment. Individual lightning strokes vary in the amounts of energy they carry. One of the most powerful strokes ever measured and recorded in the United States occurred in Pittsburgh in July 1947. This great spark of electricity, more accurately termed a surge of electrical current, yielded 345,000 amperes, or enough power to light up more than 600,000 60-watt bulbs for as long as the flash lasted. Such a spurt of tremendous power is of no practical use, however, because it is "switched on" for only a very small fraction of time.

Benjamin Franklin's little device with its hand-cranked glass sphere was the simplest of machines; an active cumulonimbus, on the other hand, is a huge and complicated electric generator. Nevertheless, in spite of the difference in size, both a thunder cloud and a friction machine like Franklin's accomplish two things: they build up charges of electricity, and at the same time separate the charges into distinct positive and negative fields.

The Cloud Generator

It may be easy to see how the glass sphere of Franklin's machine, as it revolved against its silk-covered leather pad, gave off a collection of positive charges, while a negative charge remained on the glass. It is not so easy, however, to determine exactly how a thunder cloud generates its electricity, neatly separates it into two charges of opposite signs, and temporarily stores the two charges in different parts of the cloud. As painstakingly as scientists have worked at the problem, they do not yet have all the answers. Many theories have been offered, and it may eventually be learned that thunderstorm electricity is created by a number of complex chemical and physical processes. At the present time, however, there is one easily understood explanation, acceptable to most scientists, of how the electric charges are created, separated, and stored in a thunder cloud.

You will remember that the high, cold top of a cumulonimbus cloud is composed largely of tiny ice and snow crystals.

Often mixed with these are quantities of small hailstones formed from ice-covered snow crystals and frozen raindrops. Strong upsurging winds in the cloud violently whirl all these ice particles about so that they collide and rub against one another. The rubbing, of course, produces electrical energy by knocking out negatively charged electrons from gaseous atoms and molecules. The snow and ice particles take on negative electrical charges. This leaves the gaseous molecules in the surrounding air with an excess of positive charge.

As the crystals of snow and ice and the small hailstones grow larger and heavier, they fall downward through the cloud to warmer levels, leaving behind in the top of the cloud the positively charged gaseous molecules. Now the snow and ice crystals melt to form raindrops, which still retain the negative charges of the original particles. The host of raindrops accumulating in the base of the cloud gives that region an excess of negative charge.

This is probably the principal process by which a thunderstorm becomes electrified. The result that interests us most is that the cloud gains two strong electric poles, or centers of electric charge: the positive pole at the top of the cloud, and the negative pole at its base. Between the two poles is a neutral region, a kind of electrical no man's land a mile or so in vertical thickness, where there is no excess of either positive or negative charges. This zone, or field of neutralized electricity, acts as an insulator between the strong, restless charges of the positive and negative poles.

The electrical energy of the cloud is now concentrated in the two separated poles. Between the poles there exists what scientists call strong potential difference. The charge at each pole is bursting with energy which it wants to use. These polar stores of electrical energy might be compared to great coiled springs waiting to unwind and do some sort of mechanical work. It is the habit of separate positive and negative charges of electricity to want to join their forces and neutralize each other. For this reason, when the potential difference between the positive and negative poles of a thunder cloud reaches a point of great electrical pressure, which may be anything from a hundred million to a thousand million volts, something is bound to happen.

What does happen may be one of two things. A bolt of lightning may flash between the positive and negative poles of the cloud itself, using up the stored electrical energy in light, heat, and sound, and at the same time neutralizing the opposite charges. Or the great negative charge at the base of the cloud may induce a strong positive charge on the earth below. Then both cloud and earth charges rush to meet each other in a long streak of lightning.

A single bolt of lightning removes most of the cloud's store of electrical energy, but the machinery of an active storm soon replaces it. The process of separating positive and negative charges in the cloud continues as the winds hasten to turn the crank of the huge electric generator. In the space of twenty seconds or more, the electric charges at the poles are renewed, the electric field returns to normal, and everything is ready for the crashing discharge of another bolt of lightning. This process will go on, and lightning will flash in the cloud, or between cloud and earth, so long as the updrafts in the cloud are able to keep the gears of the storm turning at top speed.

There are actually more lightning discharges within a thunder cloud than there are discharges flashed between cloud and earth. But we who live on the earth are more concerned with the latter, because they are likely to do damage, in one way or another, that can affect us.

As a vigorous thunderstorm moves over the land, the strong negative electrical charge at the bottom of the cloud induces an equally strong positive charge on the earth. Positive charges from the earth begin to race along the surface of the ground, or a few feet above it, to an area directly beneath the charge of the cloud. Billions of these electrical charges, attached to ions in the air, tear along at great speeds across fields, up the walls of buildings, along light and telephone wires, and even up such objects as animals and people. Like electrical rats following an electrical Pied Piper, the swarm of earth charges moves along, keeping up with the traveling storm, and continually gathering more charges on the way. You cannot feel this induced charge. If the charge in the atmosphere becomes very intense, it might be seen in the form of Saint Elmo's fire streaming off some pointed object. Or, if you were on the top of a building, your hair might bristle and try to stand on end.

The Lightning Flash

The electricity at the base of the cloud wants to get down to earth, and the earth charge wants desperately to rise upward to the cloud, since their main objective is to come together and neutralize each other. What keeps them apart is

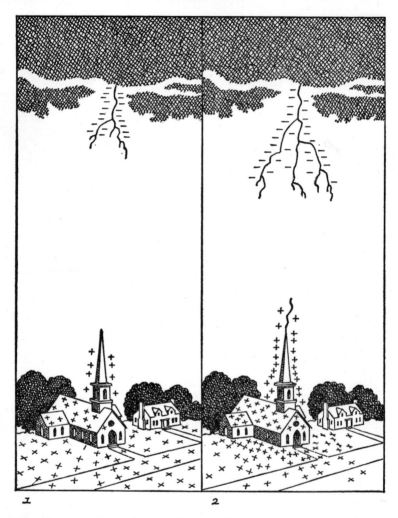

1   *2*

the three or four thousand feet of air that separates them. Although air is a better conductor of electricity in summer than at any other time of year, it is never a very willing conductor. In fact, it acts exactly like a thick insulator.

As the electrical tension, or pressure, increases between the cloud and the ground, the tough resistance of the insulating

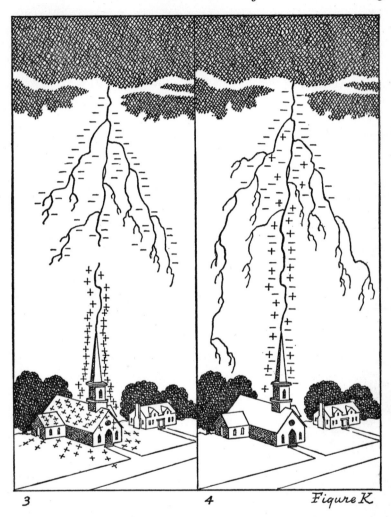

3   4   *Figure K*

air is being changed beneath the storm ceiling. Small charges leak out from the cloud and flow invisibly through the air. As this flow of electricity increases, the strong insulating quality of the air is broken down a little, preparing the way for what is to come.

When the air becomes more or less saturated with the

seeping electricity, the great discharge of energy we call a lightning stroke happens, and happens so fast that our ordinary watches cannot time it. Strangely enough, the lightning flash is not one continuous streak. It occurs in a very swift series of steps.

In the four panels of Figure K are shown something of what happens in the lightning-flash process. But to picture it as completely as possible and include all the steps, we would have to use a long strip of illustrations, like a slow-motion movie film. First of all (in Panel 1) an invisible streak of free electrons, called a "pilot streamer," shoots out of the cloud base for from fifty to seventy-five feet. By the time its energy has been used up, the pilot streamer has bored a tunnel, perhaps an inch in diameter, in the air. What is left in the tunnel is a core of ionized molecules or gases created by the action of the lightning spark.

Ordinarily, ions are created in the atmosphere by a collision between normal molecules of oxygen and nitrogen and fast-moving electrically charged particles of matter from outer space, called cosmic rays; but a powerful electric spark, such as lightning, can do the same work. In this case, the lightning drives free electrons against electrically neutral molecules in the atmosphere with enough force to knock off some of their loosely held electrons. This action produces positive ions and electrons. These new free electrons in the same manner produce more ions, and so on, until great numbers of ionized particles have been created.

The core of ions in the lightning tunnel, unlike ordinary air, is as good a conductor of electricity as a length of copper wire. Following immediately on the pilot streamer is another streamer of lightning called a leader. This leaves the cloud and plunges down the ionized tunnel, and drives farther toward the earth by another fifty feet or so, at the same time lengthening the tunnel. This happens again and again, each new streamer of lightning bringing the conducting tunnel nearer to the earth.

Meanwhile (in Panel 2), positive charges are swarming upward (from a lightning rod on a church steeple in the picture) to meet the negatively charged leader of lightning coming from the cloud. In Panel 3, the positive charge from the earth has shot up to about fifty feet, and the cloud streamer is only a couple of hundred feet above it.

Describing in words the action of a lightning flash takes a great deal of time, whereas all the tunnel-boring steps that have been described require only about $\frac{1}{100}$ of a second. And right at this point, when all the tunnel-boring is completed, the real display of thunderous fireworks is set off. The charge from the earth leaps up through the ionized tunnel (Panel 4), prepared by the cloud leaders, to join with the downcoming streak of cloud electricity. The lightning flashes you see are actually the return strokes from the earth shooting up to the cloud.

Following the first return stroke of lightning there are usually three to six minor strokes, although a severe discharge may exhibit as many as forty. Combined, these strokes represent a terrific flow of electric current. Since the lightning we see travels at about 1860 miles a second, all the strokes appear as a single flash to our eyes.

This blinding flash of lightning may last from $\frac{1}{500}$ of a second to $1\frac{1}{2}$ seconds, depending upon how many return strokes there are. It is our eyes that play tricks on us in giving us the impression that lightning leaps from the sky to the ground. The leaders do push down from the cloud, but they are invisible because they give almost no light. Only the return strokes that rush from earth to cloud create a visible brilliance. The tunnel, or ionized path, that lightning creates and uses as an electrical conductor is not large. It may be as small in diameter as a piece of string, or as thick as a man's wrist.

Besides making a brilliant light, lightning also produces the very loud noise we call thunder. Scientists say that about three-quarters of the energy of a lightning bolt is expended in heating the very narrow channel of air which it follows. In just a few millionths of a second, the temperature around a streamer of lightning rises to about 27,000 degrees Fahrenheit. This is rather hot, considering that the temperature at the surface of the sun is only 10,000 degrees! The great heat produced by lightning causes the air in the channel to expand in a sudden explosion. And, as with all types of explosions, powerful sound waves are set in motion.

Sight and Sound

The sound of thunder can ordinarily be heard for a distance of six or seven miles. In very quiet summer air, however, low rumbles can be detected from as far away as twenty miles. The rumbling sound so characteristic of thunder may be due to a number of causes. The repeated heating up of the air tunnel by a series of return strokes may be responsible. Or the echoes of a loud crash, coming from various portions of the cloud base, could produce an effect of vibrating or rolling sound. Mountain slopes, too, act as reflectors of sound, creating rumbling echoes of thunder. One thing is certain, thunder is not the noise of Henry Hudson's ghostly little crew playing at ninepins in the high Catskills!

The lightning flash reaches our eyes almost instantly, but the sound of the thunder, which is created with the flash, travels much more slowly, at about 1100 feet per second. If you can count 5 seconds between seeing the flash and hearing the thunder, you know that the bolt was 5500 feet, or little over a mile away.

If you have a good faculty for "filtering out" different types of sound, you may hear sounds other than the familiar one of thunder connected with a lightning flash. Just preceding the thunder there is often a noise as if someone were tearing a bed sheet. This is given off by the flickering leaders stepping down from the sky. Then there is also a marked click given by the upsurging streamers of electrical charge from the earth rushing to meet the leader from the sky, and the final sound of a smartly cracking whip as the return stroke jumps to the cloud, followed by the boom and roll of thunder.

As mentioned before, instead of stepping their way toward the earth to connect with an upward surge of electricity, many bolts of lightning discharge themselves in the cloud. This most often happens when the base of the thunderstorm is so high above the earth that a lightning discharge can more easily jump from the bottom to the top of the charged cloud, or from the top down, than struggle to overcome the insulating air between cloud and earth. The brilliant streamers of the cloud lightning are usually hidden by the thick walls of the cloud. All we see is a bright glow, a broad sheet of illuminated cloud. This is what is commonly called "sheet lightning." Some people refer to it as "heat lightning," but it has nothing whatever to do with the warmth of the summer night when it is observed.

The form of lightning flash most frequently seen is the discharge between cloud and earth, and is known as forked or streak lightning. The main streak, appearing to zigzag downward, often has a number of forks or branches shooting out from it. The branches are also struggling to connect with

Figure L

the earth charge. Sometimes the lowest branches do reach the earth charge and strike objects quite far away from where the large central bolt hit, as shown in Figure L.

The flickering of the lightning flash, which is so often noticed, is an effect that is produced by the repetition of return strokes in the flash. The bolt, or flash, may last for a second, although it is not actually discharging electricity steadily all the time. What is seen as a single flash is made up of a number of very brief separate strokes that "blink" at intervals of about $\frac{1}{30}$ of a second. These quick, separate strokes generally follow the path of the original ionized channel. Instead of the usual three or four separate strokes, there may be a dozen or more. It is the lighting up of the channel by successive strokes that causes the flicker. The effect would be much the same on a movie screen if the projector were slowed down to about one-half of its usual speed.

On some occasions, especially over rather dry regions, lightning will dart from the base of a storm and travel

Figure M

horizontally beneath the cloud in a forked streamer without attempting to turn toward the earth. Sometimes these strange flashes will merely end in mid-air eight or ten miles from their starting point. At other times they may turn upward into another part of the cloud where a strong positive electrical charge has been brought down from the top by falling rain, as pictured in Figure M. On rare occasions one of these wandering bolts of lightning may travel for as much as twenty miles. It started, of course, from the base of a thunder cloud, but the far end of its forked streamer may be in clear air and far from the parent cloud. Here the end of the flash will suddenly leap down to earth. Since there is blue sky directly overhead, people in the vicinity of the wandering lightning stroke are naturally mystified. This sort of flash gave rise to the old notion that lightning can come from a cloudless sky, and consequently led to the coining of the well-known expression "a bolt from the blue."

Balls of Lightning

An even stranger belief is that lightning can appear as hurtling balls of fire during a thunderstorm. So far, no scientist has ever seen one, and scientists in general believe that it is impossible for lightning to take on such a form. But people without scientific knowledge and lacking in trained observation are too often at the mercy of their imaginations. The brilliant light from a close-by flash of lightning can leave a circular image of light on the retina of the eye which may last for several seconds. It is easy to see that someone's imagination might turn this impression into a ball of fire. In telling about his experience, the observer quite innocently dresses up the story with details of his own concocting to make it more convincing, and so the belief in ball lightning becomes established, and, like many another product of popular imagination, stories about fireballs are endlessly repeated and credulously accepted as real happenings.

Most stories about ball lightning are amusingly fantastic. The balls, it seems, vary in size from an inch to six feet in diameter. They may be white, blue, purple, yellow, or red. As they move slowly or rapidly through the air or over the ground, they tend to bounce like basketballs. Sometimes they are said to explode with a deafening blast.

One typical story concerns two elderly ladies, Miss Janie and Miss Sally, who were very much afraid of thunderstorms. One summer afternoon, when a storm was in progress, they were startled out of their wits when a blue fireball (they later said) came down the chimney of their house, rolled out of the fireplace, and bounced around the living room. From there it scooted with a swishing sound through an open door and into another room, leaving behind it smell of burning sulphur.

At the first appearance of the ball, Miss Janie collapsed in a chair and threw her shawl over her head. Miss Sally, no doubt busily skittering about in an effort not to collide with the ball of lightning, nevertheless kept her presence of mind. As soon as the fearfully glowing thing passed through the doorway, she lunged forward and slammed shut the door. Then, somewhat breathlessly, she said, "You can take off your shawl, Janie. I've got the thing shut up in the kitchen!"

7. THE GOOD, THE BAD, AND THE CURIOUS

The Impartial Cumulonimbus

There are few people in the world who have never experienced a thunderstorm, since such storms are fairly well distributed over the inhabited portions of the globe. Meteorologists estimate that 6 million thunderstorms occur each year around our planet. This means that, on the average, 16,438 electrical storms happen every day; and that during any one hour approximately 685 such storms are pouring down rain and shooting 100 bolts of lightning earthward in various regions of the world.

Some portions of the globe are visited by more thunderstorms than others during a year. The island of Java, for instance, which is about the size of Maryland, outstrips all other spots in the number of electrical storms. Thunder rolls somewhere on the island 223 days out of 365. Central and South Africa, Southern Mexico, Panama, and Central Brazil are also well blessed with thunder and lightning. In our own country, Florida and the states that lie along the Gulf of Mexico are quite thundery regions.

In colder regions, however, such as the northern Scandinavian countries, Iceland and Greenland, and the far north in Canada, thunder is very seldom heard. In fact, people who live north of the Arctic Circle might be expected to hear the boom of thunder once in about ten years. What amazement this must cause—as exciting as a snowfall in central Florida.

Ships well out at sea encounter few thunderstorms over the oceans, although such storms do frequently occur in some seasons off the southern coast of Brazil and over the sea in the vicinity of the East Indies and Madagascar.

The thunderstorm is without doubt nature's largest single bundle of power. Most of its energy, fortunately, is expended high over our heads. Some of it reaches the earth in the form of rain and hail. But the portion of its force that awes and affects us most is lightning, whether it comes from ordinary thunderstorms, tornadoes, or hurricanes. Considering the tremendous electric current in a bolt of lightning, its explosive force, and the great heat it generates in the fraction of a second, it is not strange that most of us have a hearty respect for, if not fear of, it.

Like all other great forces in nature, lightning has a very important place in the scheme of things. But according to purely human ideas it is unpredictable and thoroughly dangerous, especially if we happen to be right in its path. We can learn, however, to be reasonably safe from the effects of its fiery streamers. Moreover, the greater our knowledge of its habits, the more fascinating the subject becomes, even though its whimsical nature and its curious delight in playing pranks can be both amusing and frighteningly exciting at times.

Stories of lightning's practical jokes, large and small, are fairly reliable, because lightning leaves behind it enough visible evidence to help tell the tale. Meteorologists are apt to describe lightning as erratic. In other words, you can never be sure of what it will do when it hits something. Some years ago lightning struck a house and entered a bedroom. A woman, with her hair done up in metal curlers, was asleep in bed. No physical harm was done to the woman, but the lightning heated the curlers and gave her a quick permanent.

In Turkey, lightning came into the kitchen of a restaurant. Nothing in the room was affected except for two dozen eggs lying in a pottery bowl. They were thoroughly cooked. In upper New York State, a bolt of lightning hit a house and set it afire, then jumped to a pole to which was attached a metal fire-alarm box. The switch in the box was immediately melted together and rang the proper fire alarm at the fire station.

Then there was the farm in New Jersey where a man was enjoying the evening paper beside his favorite reading lamp. Outside a thunderstorm was in full swing. Suddenly lightning surged in on the house wiring to the lamp and singed the reader's hair to a close crewcut. Aside from a case of fright, the farmer suffered no ill effects.

The list of roguish pranks played by lightning is endless, but strikes involving people do not always have happy endings. They are often tragic. Lightning, after all, is an electric current, and it often represents energy measured in thousands of amperes. This is vast power indeed when one recalls that the electricity in use in homes amounts to only about 15 amperes. It is well to remember, too, that it is the invariable habit of lightning to find a path of least resistance to the earth. For that reason it seeks out high objects like trees and steeples, follows exposed wires, leaps to things made of metal, and sometimes passes through people's bodies because they present less resistance than air, which normally is not a good conductor.

One statement about lightning to forget is the old saying that lightning never strikes in the same place twice. The best evidence that this is untrue is New York City's Empire State Building. This 1472-foot-tall structure has been struck as many as twelve times during a single storm, and has taken as many as fifty hits in the course of a year.

Some Precautions

Although the chance that you may be harmed by lightning is no greater than about 1 in 370,000, it is wise to take care by obeying a few simple rules. The main rule, of course, is not to stay out-of-doors when a thunderstorm moves in. You may be the highest object around, and just exactly what the next bolt of lightning is looking for as a quick conductor to the ground. If you are in open country, do not shelter under a tree. If the tree is struck, several unpleasant things can happen to you. Lightning can leap from the tree to your body, or it can surge into your body from the ground after spreading out from the tree. Or you may luckily escape from the shock of lightning but be badly injured by flying chunks of timber if the tree is shattered. And it can be completely shattered.

Hilltops are "hot spots" during a thunderstorm. So are wire

fences. Lightning can electrify a wire fence for long distances—far from the scene of the strike. Cows and horses are often killed because they were close to a fence during a storm. Being on a beach is an invitation to the sharp end of a thunderbolt. And, whatever you do, do not go swimming during an electrical storm. Strong currents from lightning can travel through water for quite a distance before they lose their lethal energy. Even if the current merely stuns you, you then are in grave danger of drowning.

If you can find the shelter of an all-steel automobile, you are a lucky fugitive from a storm. Should the car be struck, its metal body will safely carry the charge to the earth. With no shelter of any kind in sight, you are less likely to be harmed if you lie flat on the ground than if you stay standing up. A soaking by rain is not nearly so uncomfortable as becoming a human lightning rod! And do not overlook the fact that rubbers or rubber boots will not insulate you from a thunderbolt. Lightning may find it practical to use the upper part of you as a conductor, then jump over the rubber to the ground, just as it jumps the tires of an automobile.

At home, you are normally quite safe in the house, especially if you are at the center of the room. The walls are a more convenient conductor for lightning than you would be. The old idea that shutting all the windows will prevent lightning from coming in is not at all true. Unless the house is equipped with lightning rods, or there is a television aerial on the roof, the chimney is usually the tallest portion of the house. In the event of a hit, lightning would be apt to descend the flue into a fireplace or a stove. When a storm is in action these are objects to stay away from. Although electric and telephone lines are usually well grounded, it is probably wiser not to use radios or telephones when an electrical storm threatens. And since water pipes are easy pathways for lightning in some instances, taking a shower or tub bath, or washing dishes, is inviting trouble.

Something about Lightning Rods

Benjamin Franklin's invention, the lightning rod, will not prevent a bolt of lightning from seeking out a house or a barn. If lightning does strike, however, a rod system will carry the powerful electric current down to the earth without the danger of setting fire to the house or of damaging it in other ways. As you drive through the country, you may see rather odd-looking lightning rods sprouting from the roof ridges of old houses and barns. They are usually tall and slender, and are apt to be decorated with useless colored glass balls. One could guess, and come close to being right, that these rods were installed fifty or sixty years ago, when lightning-rod salesmen were as plentiful and dishonest as the peddlers who sold wooden nutmegs. The glass balls were supposed to be "insulators" for repelling lightning, which of course is sheer nonsense. An examination of one of these rods would probably disclose the fact that it was not only insufficiently grounded, but improperly arranged on the house as well.

Modern lightning rods consist of short, heavy metal spikes placed on the highest part of a building so as to give the greatest radius of protection. Each spike is welded to copper cables that run down the outside walls of the building, and are supported on ceramic insulators. The lower end of each cable is attached to a thick plate of copper which is buried five to ten feet in a pit filled with charcoal. The plate and the charcoal enable the lightning discharge from the cable to spread quickly and harmlessly through the earth.

Many buildings of today stand as their own lightning rods. These structures are built of stone, concrete, or glass around a framework of steel beams and girders. The steel forms an excellent network of conductors from roof to foundation, and is of course efficiently connected with the earth. When a great bolt of lightning strikes the Empire State Building, the million-volt current follows the steel down through 102 stories to the ground and no one in the building knows that several thousand amperes of electricity have just flowed past —perhaps within arm's reach.

Lightning rods are installed, too, on valuable and historic trees. Twenty-three trees on the grounds of Mount Vernon are protected in this way, including ten which were planted by George Washington. Roaming through a stretch of woodland, you may easily distinguish a tree that has suffered a strike by lightning. The injury appears usually as a deep, rough groove made by the discharge, which ran down the bark to the base of the tree. Sometimes a furrow in the earth can be seen, where the lightning left the tree and plowed up the ground.

Some scientists are of the opinion that the groove in the bark is caused by lightning following a stream of rain water that is passing down one side of the trunk. The intense heat of the lightning would turn the water to steam of sufficient force to blow away the bark along the path. If the bark is not wet enough to help carry the discharge, lightning takes another course: it may pass its powerful current through the sap of the tree. When this happens, the sap is instantly converted to steam with such explosive energy that most of the bark is blown off and the body of the trunk is split and splintered.

Seeding a Thunderstorm

Unfortunately, almost a thousand forest fires a year are caused by lightning in the northwestern United States, especially in the states of Oregon and Washington. In great stands of timber, when trees are struck by lightning, it streaks to the earth and often kindles a fire in the dry carpet of fir and spruce needles on the forest floor. Scientists are now working on ways to prevent such fires, which destroy large areas of valuable timber. It is possible to spot high, fast-moving thunderstorms before they reach the forest lands, and to send up planes equipped to "seed" the clouds with dry ice and silver iodide pellets.

Seeding a growing thundercloud scatters its energy before its generating system can build up to the point of producing lightning. The dropping of seeding chemicals into the top of a towering cumulus cloud causes the formation of large quantities of snow crystals. These grow rapidly and fall into lower and warmer regions of the cloud, where they melt into raindrops and help to trigger off the production of other raindrops. So, instead of being allowed to develop naturally into a fire-belching storm, a seeded cloud is tamed into a harmless piece of weather that dissipates itself by evaporation and with mild showers of rain as it moves over timbered areas.

In similar ways, scientists have been able to seed suspicious cumulus clouds in the neighborhood of Western wheat fields, where strong winds from thunderstorms can flatten a maturing crop, and hail can completely shell out ripe grain on the ground.

It may be possible, too, that violent cousins of the thunderstorm, tornadoes and hurricanes, can be softened or broken up in their early stages by chemically seeding them. It would be equivalent to sending up interceptor planes to destroy enemy aircraft before they could dump their bombs on a city or town. Certainly a great deal of property damage and loss of life could be prevented.

Fulgurites

If you took the time to explore carefully stretches of very sandy country, such as ocean beaches, the sand hills in the Piedmont of North and South Carolina, or dunes of the Kalahari Desert in South Africa, you might be lucky enough to find specimens of a fascinating product of lightning. What you would look for are rather long, hard, pebbly tubes called fulgurites. The word fulgurite comes from the Latin name for thunderbolt, *fulgur*, and means a mineral made by lightning.

The production of fulgurites is an interesting story. When a streamer of lightning strikes an area of dry sand, the intense heat of the streamer acts somewhat like an electric furnace. The lightning discharge is seeking moist earth, and so it

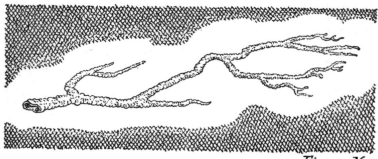

Figure N

drills a snakelike hole in the upper layer of dry sand. Heat from the flash melts the grains of sand surrounding the hole into a rough glassy tube. Fulgurites have been found that were six and eight feet long, and some of them were branched like the one shown in Figure N. Usually the diameter of the glasslike tube is smaller than two inches, and the walls of the tube are less than one-sixteenth of an inch in thickness. One has the temptation to call fulgurites "fossil lightning," but scientist friends, while they would enjoy the joke, no doubt, might think such paleontology a bit on the queer side.

The Virtues of Lightning

Things in nature are often described as either "bad" or "good." This is because, as discriminating human beings, we compare things according to a scale of our own making: as to whether we are pleased or displeased, comfortable or uncomfortable, frightened or entertained. For instance, people generally, and for no very logical reason, are fond of birds but heartily dislike snakes; yet both creatures are valuable and equally interesting. Nature, in the employment of her vast plan, however, plays no favorites. She is quite impartial.

As for lightning, we are apt to fear its power and judge it by the destruction it causes. Yet lightning accomplishes many good deeds of immense benefit. For example, lightning manufactures from the air about 100 million tons of very valuable nitrogen fertilizer each year.

The air around us is composed of gases. Except for small amounts of carbon dioxide and some rare elements, it consists largely of about four parts nitrogen and one part oxygen. The heat from a bolt of lightning combines the oxygen and the nitrogen chemically with rain. The rain brings the fixed nitrogen to the earth. Commercial fertilizer manufacturers have successfully imitated nature's lightning to get nitrogen from the air. They employ a system which discharges large electric sparks continually. Yet, over the world, lightning produces greater quantities of nitrogen compounds than all the fertilizer plants put together. Nature's fertilizer is so important a product that many botanists believe that none of the plant life on the earth could exist without it.

Meteorologists in the United States Weather Bureau have done some expert speculating upon another beneficial activity of lightning in thunderstorms. Were it not for the active flock of thunderstorms distributed around the world, particles of harmful chemical substances in the form of dust, smoke, and gases would increase to such an extent that animals and people could be poisoned by the air they breathed. During a thunderstorm these particles become electrically charged and are drawn out of the atmosphere to earth. It is the same process that modern manufacturing plants use when they pass an electric current through smoke and gases in a factory chimney. Harmful particles in the flue receive a strong charge and are collected on an oppositely charged metal grid, and so do not float out to pollute the air above a city or town.

From the viewpoint of pure science, the study of lightning has revealed a good deal about the world's electrical system. As we have seen, lightning begins under our shoes and high above our heads. There is electricity in the earth and in the atmosphere. Under normal conditions, our heads are bobbing about in air which is charged with approximately 200 volts of electricity. It is even in the ionosphere, which is a vast shell of thin gas that encloses the earth from about 200,000 feet to 200 miles above its surface. Ordinarily, the atmosphere and the ionosphere both have an excess charge of positive electricity, while the earth has an excess charge of negative electricity. If left to themselves, the ionosphere and the atmosphere would bleed off their charges to the earth, so that all of the world's supply of electricity could be neutralized in a very short time. This would amount to creating a kind of electrical vacuum.

There is an old and quite truthful saying that nature abhors a vacuum. And so the six million thunderstorms that shoot their bolts of lightning every year take care of the situation. Each thunderstorm collects and neatly separates immense quantities of electricity and succeeds in pumping positive charges back into the atmosphere and the ionosphere, while it drops fresh negative charges to earth. So the electrical balance of nature is maintained.

Man-made Lightning

To study lightning's habits, large manufacturers of electrical equipment, like General Electric and Westinghouse, create man-made lightning in high-voltage laboratories. But, unlike Franklin's little generator that produced modest voltage, the generators of the General Electric laboratory at Pittsfield, Massachusetts, are immense machines capable of turning out charges of 15 million volts. In the modern laboratory scientists work with two generators. One manufactures electricity of a positive charge, while the other produces electricity of a negative charge. The charge of each generator is led off to a tall condenser or storage device which is a modern version of the old Leyden jar. The two condensers stand about 50 feet apart. When the electric tension between them becomes strong enough, negative and positive charges attract each other, and a brilliant, roaring streamer of man-made lightning leaps across the laboratory. The effect is exactly the same as when a great spark of lightning connects the negative charge of a thundercloud with the induced positive charge from the earth.

The strokes of man-made lightning may not be as long as nature's bolts, but they are relatively as powerful. Because their laboratory lightning behaves in the same way as the real thing, scientists are able to experiment with new methods of protecting power lines, telephone lines, radio and television transmitters, electric motors and generators, and other equipment, from the long-reaching fingers of cloud lightning. In similar ways, the United States Air Force uses laboratory lightning to test aircraft and their electronic equipment under thunderstorm conditions. Lightning is not too serious a threat to planes, however. If they are struck, small holes might be burned in wing tips and fuselage, and the radio antenna melted, but the metal skin of the plane easily conducts the current of lightning safely away from pilots and passengers.

Certainly, in its violent moods lightning can be awesomely destructive. It can tear holes in unprotected buildings and bridges by its explosive force. It can blast apart water lines and set fire to gas mains. A thunderbolt can kindle a fire deep in a forest that will smolder for days, then suddenly flame in a rising wind to consume thousands of acres of timber. If you are afraid of lightning, it is some consolation to know that you have plenty of company among scientists who have learned to work with it. Yet, if you observe a few safety rules, the danger from lightning is not nearly so great as that from driving an automobile on our crowded highways.

There is a good deal of common sense, as well as humor, in the view of an American scientist who is perhaps as intimately acquainted with lightning as anyone: Dr. Carl B. McEachron of General Electric. Dr. McEachron once said, "If you heard the thunder, the lightning did not strike you. If you saw the lightning, it missed you. And if it did strike you, you would not have known it!"

INDEX